Michigan Forest Communities:
A Field Guide and Reference

Donald I. Dickmann
Department of Forestry
Michigan State University
East Lansing, MI 48824-1222

MICHIGAN STATE
UNIVERSITY
EXTENSION

ISBN No. 1-56525-019-2

© Michigan State University Extension, 2004

....

In memory of C. Frank Brockman (1902-1985),

professor of forestry at the University of Washington,

who taught me to know the forests I love.

CONTENTS

CONTENTS

*O*ne does not travel down the trail to a book alone. Many people gave me help, advice, and counsel along the way. To all of them I am indebted. Richard Kobe reviewed my initial outline and gave positive feedback about my approach to the subject. Dennis Albert, Bill Botti, Russell Kidd, Doug Pearsol, Jan Schultz, and Pat Valencia helped me locate several forest communities of which I was unaware. I also thank Jan and Raoul LePage for introducing me to Dead Man's Hill and the superb vista it provides of the Jordan River Valley. These places have joined my list of favorites among Michigan's forested treasures. Ray Miller allowed me the use of one of the Upper Peninsula Tree Improvement Center's vehicles for travel in that part of the state. Having piloted myself to Escanaba, I had to find some way to travel on the ground.

I obtained photos from Phil Huber, Kari Brown, Rick Baetsen, the State Archives of Michigan, and The Michigan Nature Conservancy. Most of the photos I took myself and in the process finally began to learn the intricacies of my digital camera. The Michigan Natural Features Inventory generously provided vegetation maps of the state. Bob Doepker and Craig Albright gave me a copy of the MIWILD (Michigan Wildlife Habitats) CD, which was very useful.

David Rothstein, Dennis Albert, and Doug Pearsol freely gave their time to read and critique the completed manuscript. Their comments and suggestions greatly helped clear up ambiguities and errors. I sincerely appreciate their efforts.

I am especially appreciative of the climate of scholarship that exists in the Michigan State University (MSU) Department of Forestry and for the support and encouragement of Daniel Keathley, department chair. Once again Elwood Ehrle—patron of botanical research and administrator of the Hanes Fund—came to my aid by granting travel funds for necessary fieldwork throughout the state. This project could not have gone forward without the support of Randy Heatley, MSU Agriculture and Natural Resources (ANR) Technical Services manager, who agreed at the outset to cover the publication costs.

The editorial, design, and production work of the staff of MSU ANR Communications & Technology Services—Alicia Burnell, Ken Fettig, and Leslie Johnson—requires special acknowledgment. Their enthusiasm, helpful suggestions, cheery demeanor, and professional attitude always made me feel very confident about the outcome of this project.

Finally, I thank my wife, Kathleen McKevitt, and our Welsh Corgi, Benny, for companionship on various forest treks. They patiently put up with my preoccupation for places forested and willingly stood by (or sniffed the scents of forest creatures) during many photo stops. Occasionally—if the setting was pleasing—I could even entice them to pose.

*F*orests are the defining natural feature of Michigan's landscape. Before European settlement began in the 17th century, forests blanketed approximately 95 percent of the state's 36.3 million acres. These forests, at first viewed as an impediment to settlement, soon became a major economic engine for the state's development. They continue in that role today. At the beginning of the 21st century, after several hundred years of human exploitation and deforestation, approximately half of the state remains covered by trees. But that's not the whole story. As one travels north through the Lower Peninsula and west through the Upper Peninsula, the land becomes increasingly forested.

Forests are continually changing, usually slowly, but sometimes abruptly. Here a tornado was the instrument of change.

The extremes of this continuum are striking—only 21 percent of the southern Lower Peninsula is occupied by patchy woods and wetland corridors, whereas 88 percent of the western Upper Peninsula is covered by extensive, largely unbroken forests.

Today's forests are different in more than extent from those that provided food, shelter, fuel, and a host of other benefits to the state's native people and then to the European immigrants who dispossessed them. Most of our current forests are relatively young, having regrown following the devastating, century-long period of logging and fire that began about the time Michigan became a state in 1837. Many of these **second-growth** forests have been harvested again, with a third-growth underway. Thus, ancient or **old-growth** forests, which were common two centuries ago, now are rare. Many of the magnificent pine forests of yesteryear have been replaced with woodlands dominated by aspen or oaks. Open savanna forests and barrens have virtually disappeared. Yet in spite of these changes, Michigan's forests remain robust and incredibly diverse. In fact, Michigan contains more vegetation types than any other state in the Midwest (Faber-Langendoen 2001).

Although changes in the state's forest cover over the past two centuries are largely due to human action, they illustrate an important ecological principle that would hold even if no humans occupied Michigan's pleasant peninsulas: forests are dynamic, not static. Thus, we can sustain and protect forests, but we cannot preserve them. Preservation implies retaining something in a facsimile of its present condition, such as canning a peach or freezing a salmon. In fact, changes will occur in our favorite woods whether we like it or not, and sometimes these changes will be abrupt, dramatic, and destructive. But the forest, in one form or another, will continue.

Having used the previous field guides in the MSU Extension series—snakes; frogs, toads, and salamanders; turtles and lizards; and butterflies and skippers—I decided that a popular guide to Michigan forest communities was needed, since none currently exists. The comprehensive *A Field Guide to Eastern Forests* by Kricher (1998)—a title in Houghton Mifflin's Peterson field guide series—and *The Field Guide to Wildlife Habitats of the Eastern United States* by Benyus partially fill the bill. But because of their broad geographic scope, the forest communities found in Michigan are painted with a fairly broad brush. I wanted something more focused and detailed. *Wisconsin's Natural Communities* by Randy Hoffman (2002) is more encompassing than Kricher or Benyus, but the focus is on Michigan's sister Great Lakes state. The beautiful coffee table book *Wildflowers of the Western Great Lakes Region* by Wells, Case, and Mellichamp (1999) is structured around natural habitats and therefore comes closest to the mark, but it's not suitable for field use. Finally, the guide by Burger and Kotar (2003) is too technical for the average reader.

A perusal of the shelves in the nature section of any bookstore reveals numerous guides to tree identification and lore. All of these resources are excellent, but they provide limited information about how trees grow together to form **forest communities**; i.e., the context of the trees largely is missing. It is the intent of this guidebook to fill this gap.

I had another reason for writing this guide. A colleague in the Department of Forestry at MSU—Larry Leefers—and I wrote a book titled *The Forests of Michigan* (2003), in which we traced the history, ecology, management, and economic importance of the state's forests. Our intent was to use this book as the text in a course on Michigan's forests (FOR 101) that we teach at MSU and also to fill a wide-open niche in the book market. It occurred to me

To know a Michigan forest is to love it.

that a companion field guide would be a nice way to round out the forest story. One could read through *The Forests of Michigan* in an evening as background, then the following day take this guide and others into the field for an up-close session in forest natural history.

To know forests is to love them. My hope is that this guide will be an avenue toward that knowledge and that out of it will come a deeper appreciation of the need to manage Michigan's rich forest diversity in a sustainable way. Mismanagement brought on by unrestrained greed or the ever-widening specter of urban sprawl and land fragmentation are serious threats to Michigan forests. Does this mean that forests and people should not mix? The answer, of course, is a resounding NO! As a forester, I am committed to sustainable forest management, whether that means cutting a tree down for manufacture into two-by-fours as part of a silvicultural plan or, at the other extreme, restricting entry into a wooded tract to protect an endangered species. Forests are there to enrich our lives, both in a commodity and a non-commodity sense, but they also have intrinsic values—they have a right to exist for their own sake.

After a brief history of Michigan forests, I will discuss the ecological factors that regulate the distribution, structure, and composition of the forest communities (**forest types**) that exist in Michigan today. After a discussion of the

Wildflowers add a bright splash of color to the otherwise muted tones of Michigan forest communities.

concept of a forest community type—in particular, the dynamic aspect of this concept—I will go on to describe 23 distinct forest communities that can be found across the state. Each community will be illustrated with photographs and maps. Certain forest communities—e.g., mesic northern hardwoods—are broadly distributed and will receive more extensive treatment. Other forest types are rare and very localized—e.g., Great Lakes barrens—and their coverage will be more limited. The focus of each community discussion will be on its characteristic plants—trees, shrubs, and herbs. I also will discuss the distribution of each type and common forest management activities (**silviculture**) applied to them.

A SHORT HISTORY
OF MICHIGAN FORESTS

*T*he diverse forests that cover much of the Michigan landscape are the culmination of many thousands of years of development. Their history begins with the slow melting and retreat of the **Wisconsin glacier**, a portentous event that marked the end of the great **Pleistocene Ice Age**. The spoil left behind by the retreating glacier represented a biological vacuum; plants and animals that had marked time for millennia in ice-free areas south of the glacier lost no time in moving north to invade the vacated landscape. Among these first plants were several types of trees, the ancestors of today's Michigan forests.

The glacier began its retreat about 14,000 years ago. Most of the Lower Peninsula was ice-free about 2,000 years later (Kapp 1999). At this time a narrow belt of tundra and scattered clumps of spruce and tamarack occupied much of the northern Lower Peninsula, with closed boreal forests of spruce, fir, birch, and poplar to the south. After the passage of another 2,000 years, the glacial margin had receded almost to the shore of Lake Superior in the Upper Peninsula. Boreal conifers still dominated in the north, but now the southern part of the state was occupied by more complex pine-

Spruce and tamarack forests were among the first to establish after the Wisconsin glacier receded.

From about 1850 to 1910, virtually all of Michigan's virgin forests were cut down or destroyed by wildfires.

hardwood forests on the uplands and swamp forests inland from Saginaw Bay and lakes St. Clair and Erie. Approximately 3,500 years ago, Michigan forests began to take on a look that would be familiar to today's observer, though species such as beech and hemlock, which migrated northward slowly, probably still would have been uncommon in the Upper Peninsula.

Humans have continuously occupied Michigan's forests almost from their icy beginnings. Through the processes of cultural evolution and migration, these Paleo-Indian people became the native tribes—mostly Ojibwe, Odawa, and Bodewademi—encountered by the first French explorers in the 17th century. Indian people intensively used the forests they lived in for their daily needs. They also cleared land for agriculture and set fires, some of which burned over large areas. But because

the tribal populations were relatively small and their ethical attitude towards the land was beneficent, their overall impacts were negligible. That all changed when the flood of immigrants from Europe and the eastern states into Michigan began in the early 19th century. These people brought with them a new, three-faceted plan for land and forests: get rid of the Indians, exploit Michigan's prime timber for economic gain, and clear the land for farming. So began the sorriest chapter in Michigan's forest history.

During the last half of the 19th and the first decades of the 20th centuries, the Euro-Christian plan was carried out with a vengeance. Indian people, already decimated by European diseases to which they had little resistance, were killed, swindled out of their land birthright, or forcibly moved to locations outside the state. Meanwhile,

© Rick Baetsen

the timber barons and their legions of shanty boys felled every tree that could make them a buck. And farmers cleared land any way they could, frequently using fire. These fires frequently erupted into conflagrations that burned over thousands—sometime millions—of acres. By the 1920s and '30s, a vast area of Michigan's "pleasant peninsulas" was a wasteland of charred stumps, second-growth brushland, and abandoned farms.

Once extirpated from Michigan forests, the pine marten has come back, with help from wildlife biologists.

The story, fortunately, does not end at this low point. Nature is amazingly robust, and with some help from foresters, Michigan's forests came back. The magnificent stands of pine that the timber barons so lusted after are mostly gone, however, replaced by millions of acres of aspen and oaks. Planting of pine by the Civilian Conservation Corps and other government agencies in the 1930s, '40s, and '50s went some distance to recoup these loses. Many of these plantations now contain large trees reminiscent of their 18th-century progenitors. Northern forests that were dominated by hardwoods before European settlement came back largely true to form, missing only the heavily exploited white pines and hemlocks. Southern forests also were reincarnated, although much diminished in scale in their urban-agricultural setting. Even animals such as the pine marten and the timber wolf, extirpated during the orgy of destruction, reside once again in Michigan's woods.

By and large, the forests we see today in Michigan are still recovering from the unprecedented 19th and early 20th century period of exploitation and destruction or subsequent harvests. Nonetheless, they are bountiful and wondrous in their own right. With the sustainable management philosophy that prevails today and the regulation of forest practices by government, it is highly unlikely that they will again meet the fate of their 19th century predecessors. But we must be vigilant. When there is big money to be made either from cutting trees for timber or developing the land on which they grow, forests still can lose. As a career-long university professor, I am committed to the principle that knowledge can help prevent such loses. Hence this little book.

*T*o understand Michigan forest communities, we must have some notion of the ecological factors that cause one community to differ from others. These factors include elements of geology, climate, and biology (including humans), which all interact to form forest **habitats**. These habitats and the communities of organisms that occur in them are together referred to as **ecosystems**.

Glaciation

The lasting imprint of the Pleistocene Ice Age is the underlying physical factor that determines Michigan forest habitats and the vegetation that grows in them. At its farthest extension some 16,000 years ago, the great Wisconsin glacier covered all of Michigan. Therefore, every habitat in the state is glacially derived, either directly or indirectly. The glacier left behind numerous landforms that directly influence the type and distribution of forest communities:

• **Ice-contact features** were formed by direct action of the glacier and vary from steeply hilly to gently rolling. They include **moraines, drumlins, kames, eskers, crevasse fillings**, and **till plains**. The material that makes up these features—glacial till—consists of variable, unstratified (unlayered) mixtures of clay, sand, gravel, and rocks.

• **Outwash plains** were formed by the action of braided meltwater streams flowing from beneath the glacier. They are flat or gently rolling and consist of stratified or layered glacial sediments, mostly sand and gravel.

• Partially buried ice blocks that broke off from the glacier formed depressions in outwash or till plains called **kettles**. When the ice melted, lakes or ponds formed. Many kettles have filled in with partially decayed vegetation (muck or peat), forming bogs or swampy wetlands.

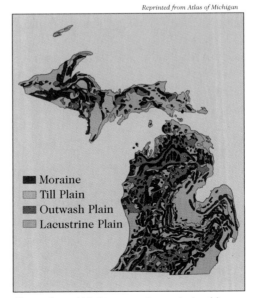

Reprinted from Atlas of Michigan

■ Moraine
▢ Till Plain
■ Outwash Plain
▢ Lacustrine Plain

The surface of Michigan consists entirely of formations that were directly or indirectly derived from the Wisconsin glacier.

• The melting glacier formed large lakes, most of which drained to form flat or undulating, silty or sandy **lake beds** or **lacustrine plains**. Lake beds also were exposed when the land, relieved of the tremendous weight of the glacier, rose along shallow shores of the Great Lakes and the water levels of the lakes dropped.

• In some places—especially in the Upper Peninsula—underlying **bedrock**, scraped and polished by the glacier, was exposed.

• Long after the glacier was gone, wave action and on-shore winds caused **sand dunes** to form along the shores of the Great Lakes and some inland lakes.

Climate

During the millennia following the retreat of the glacier, climate—the sum total of sunlight, precipitation, wind, and atmospheric deposition—has acted upon exposed landforms, modifying them in various ways. Glacial till has become weathered by the action of climate and the organisms that have grown in it to become **soil**. Water erosion and stream action have deposited soils in downslope positions and deltas. Wind has created dunes. Thus, the raw spoil left by the glacier has been trans-

Table 1. Soil properties in relation to the continuum of ecological habitats.

Properties	Ecological Habitats				
	Xeric ◄► Dry – mesic	◄► Mesic ◄►		Wet – mesic	◄►Hydric*
Average moisture during the growing season	Very dry	Somewhat dry	Moist	Very moist; water may stand in spring	Very wet
Drainage	Excessively drained	Very well-drained	Well-drained	Somewhat poorly drained	Very poorly drained or undrained
Surface soil textures	Sand to loamy sand	Loamy sand to sandy loam	Sandy loam to loam	Loam to clay loam	Sand to clay loam or organic (muck or peat)
Natural fertility	Infertile	Moderately infertile to fertile	Very fertile	Fertile to moderately fertile	Moderately fertile to very infertile

* Hydric habitats are very complex and variable. Swamps or fens fed by flowing groundwater or surface streams may be relatively fertile and productive, although tree growth is limited by anoxic (oxygen-deficient) conditions in the soil for all or part of the growing season. On the other extreme, the thick peat soil of bogs and muskegs is strongly acid and saturated with stagnant water that is low in dissolved oxygen, severely limiting tree growth. Many hydric habitats also exist between these extremes.

formed into habitats suitable for growth of a wide range of trees and other plants. The importance of soil to life can hardly be overstated. But soils in a glacial landscape such as Michigan's vary exceedingly, even within a few yards, introducing a considerable measure of ecological complexity (Table 1).

In addition to modifying glacial landscapes over the long term, climate also directly affects plant survival and growth on a day-to-day basis. Three factors of climate can be directly linked to the distribution of forest communities. **Length of the growing season**—the number of days between the last killing frost (28 degrees F or lower) in spring and the first killing frost in the fall—varies widely in Michigan, largely

because of the effects of latitude and the influence of the Great Lakes. **Minimum winter temperatures** also control to a large degree the distribution of plants. Many Michigan hardwood

Reprinted from Atlas of Michigan

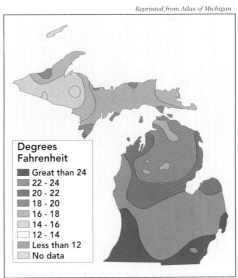

Degrees Fahrenheit
- Great than 24
- 22 - 24
- 20 - 22
- 18 - 20
- 16 - 18
- 14 - 16
- 12 - 14
- Less than 12
- No data

Mean January temperatures across Michigan are strongly influenced by the Great Lakes and latitude.

Reprinted from Atlas of Michigan

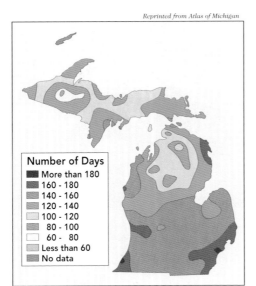

Number of Days
- More than 180
- 160 - 180
- 140 - 160
- 120 - 140
- 100 - 120
- 80 - 100
- 60 - 80
- Less than 60
- No data

Length of the growing season (number of days between the last killing frost in spring and first killing frost in autumn) varies considerably across Michigan.

trees, for example, are winter hardy only in southern Michigan and northward along the Lake Michigan shore, where temperatures are moderated. Lastly, **yearly precipitation**, although not as important as temperature, also varies across the state and influences plant distribution.

Forest habitat regions

Ecologists, recognizing the importance of glacial features and climate, have divided Michigan into four distinct habitat regions: basically the northern

Reprinted from Atlas of Michigan

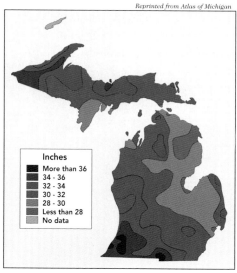

Inches
- More than 36
- 34 - 36
- 32 - 34
- 30 - 32
- 28 - 30
- Less than 28
- No data

Mean annual precipitation generally increases from northeast to southwest in the Lower Peninsula and east to west in the Upper Peninsula.

and southern halves of the Lower Peninsula and the eastern and western halves of the Upper Peninsula (Albert 1995, Barnes and Wagner 2003). Note that there is a broad **transition zone** between regions I and II—forest communities from both regions intermix in this zone, sometimes in unusual ways. Natural forests in Region I are overwhelmingly broad-leaved and **deciduous** (trees lose their leaves in the autumn), whereas in regions II, III, and IV, evergreen (with the exception of tamarack) **conifers** are common and often dominant.

Microclimate

Within any habitat region, differences in local conditions can produce substantial differences in microclimates.

For example, ridge tops and south- or west-facing slopes are hotter and drier than north- or east-facing slopes because of greater exposure to the sun. Ridge tops also are drier than downslope locations because water drains away from them. Depressions, in addition to being collectors of water, are colder than surrounding high ground because cold air drains into them. Hence the term "frost pocket." Depressions also are much more likely to produce fog. Microclimates can be particularly influential in providing habitats for species at the limits of their natural range. Yellow birch, for example, grows only in cool, wet depressions and wetlands in the southern counties of Michigan, whereas in the heart of its range in the Upper Peninsula, it is common in mesic and wet-mesic habitats as well as swamps.

Redrawn from Albert (1995) and Barnes and Wagner (1981).

Region III:
Eastern Upper Peninsula

Region IV:
Western Upper Peninsula

Region II:
Northern Lower Peninsula

Transition Zone

Region I:
Southern Lower Peninsula

The forest communities of Michigan are broadly defined by the habitat regions in which they grow.

Community dynamics

A fundamental principle of ecology is that communities are dynamic, not static. They change over time, often in major ways. The composition and structure of a forest that exists in a particular place at a particular moment can be likened to a single frame in a movie that runs on without end. A time lapse version of that movie, beginning 12,000 years ago and running to the present, would be quite lively. Forests would grow, evolve, and then in an instant vanish in a pall of smoke, the black cloud of a storm, or, more recently, the flash of a saw. In another instant, the forest would spring back to life. In some places, this cycle would be very short, maybe tens of years in real time; in others, the cycle would encompass thousands of years. These dynamic cycles of forest growth are driven by three ecological processes: secondary succession, destructive disturbances, and climate change. These processes are as pervasive today as they have ever been, and they will continue to pervade the future.

The long-term process of initiation, growth, and development of a community in a particular habitat is called succession. **Primary succession** occurs on sterile terrain that was previously unvegetated; e.g., the initial colonization by organisms of the landforms left behind by the Wisconsin glacier. **Secondary succession** occurs after an existing community is destroyed or disrupted by a disturbance. Secondary succession usually proceeds through several distinct stages, eventually forming a quasi-stable, late-successional community if another major disturbance does not occur.

A short-lived pioneer aspen community succeeding to shade-tolerant trees, predominantly sugar maple.

Early-successional (**pioneer**) forest communities establish soon after a disturbance. They usually consist of short-lived trees such as aspen, pin cherry, or paper birch. These pioneer trees usually are **intolerant** of shade; i.e., they require full sunlight to survive. **Moderately tolerant** midsuccessional communities may become established under the light shade of the early successional overstory, and as pioneer trees die, midsuccessional trees (e.g., white pine, white ash, or red maple) take over the canopy positions. Eventually these midsuccessional trees may in turn be replaced by **shade-tolerant** late-successional trees (e.g., hemlock, balsam fir, or sugar maple) and associated plants, which form a self-perpetuating community. But this general sequence is just one of many that could occur.

Kari Brown

Stand-replacing fires are major disturbances that reset the successional clock.

Succession is an extremely variable process, even in the same habitat. In certain cases, for example, the initial community that establishes following a disturbance may persist and replicate itself.

The wild cards in community dynamics are the **disturbances** that disrupt ecosystems. They can take many forms: fires, floods, straight-line windstorms, tornadoes, ice storms, insect or disease outbreaks, and animal damage. Human disturbances also are pervasive—logging, land clearing, mining, damming of rivers, wetland drainage, pollution, etc. Secondary succession begins after each major disturbance, although how it proceeds varies depending on the kind and intensity of the disturbance and the habitat in which it occurs. Some disturbances—called **stand-replacing**—are very intense and completely disrupt ecosystems, sometimes over a huge area, and lead to the establishment of pioneer communities. On the other end of the spectrum are **gap-forming** disturbances that kill only one or a few overstory trees and create a hole in the canopy that is usually filled in by trees already established in the understory. Moderate disturbances fall somewhere in the scale between these two extremes and initiate different kinds of succession.

We may view disturbances as bad because they can destroy our favorite forests and create ugliness. But in the natural scheme of things, they are as normal as sunlight and rainfall. In fact, disturbances can create forests that are exceptionally pleasing—who can resist a light, airy stand of paper birch? The important point is that ecosystems recover—secondary succession is an irrepressible force. The community that replaces the one destroyed may be different, that is true, but over a long period of time, a community resembling the original will usually evolve. If we are patient—or very long-lived—we may even see that happen.

What is a forest community type?

First of all, what is a forest? I define it as a community whose dominant plants—in size, not number—are trees. Trees may be dense and closely spaced, creating a continuous **overstory canopy** and deep shade at ground level (**closed forest**). In old, mature closed forests, several layers of **subcanopy trees** often are present under the overstory, along with a well-developed ground flora. On the other extreme, trees may be widely spaced or scattered, with a discontinuous canopy that permits lots of sun to reach the ground (**open forest** or **savanna**). In the spaces among the trees, a prairie or meadow flora flourishes. A more or less continuous gradation between these forest extremes exists. Forests also have a minimum size—usually large enough to completely eliminate environmental "edge effects" in the forest interior. However interesting, a fencerow, roadside strip of trees, or small patch of trees (less than 1 or 2 acres) in open land is not considered a forest in the context of this guidebook. Finally, forests are wild. Woodlands that are continually disturbed by livestock grazing, herbicide spraying, mowing, or trampling are not considered in this discussion.

The community types described in this book are based on mature forest characteristics.

A forest community type is a broadly defined ecosystem—a varied and complex assemblage of plants, animals, and other organisms living together in a common habitat (Barnes et al. 1998). Fundamentally, naming and describing a community type is an attempt to put a segment of the natural world in a box, always a tenuous process fraught with many pitfalls. These pitfalls should be discussed before we proceed any further.

Decay organisms are essential members of forest communities.

How are forest communities defined?

Forest community types are defined principally by their characteristic tree species. This practice does not imply that the organisms associated with these trees are somehow less important ecologically. Trees are large and structurally dominant, and they may have monetary value or aesthetic appeal; thus we focus on them. But in the natural world, every organism plays an important role. Forest communities are incredibly diverse, consisting of thousands—maybe even millions—of kinds of organisms, from one-celled microbes to huge, complex trees. Michigan contains approximately 1,800 native plants, with another 800 non-native (exotic) plants added to the mix. Unfortunately, only a few of the best known and most recognizable plants can be included in my description of each type. Furthermore, each person's background and interests influence his or her choice of what organisms should be included in the description (e.g., see Hoffman 2002 and Kricher 1998).

A second difficulty with forest typing concerns the inevitable variation that occurs in the field. Forested landscapes present a continuum of vegetation; the transition from one type to another is sometimes gradual, sometimes abrupt. How should we handle transition communities? In addition, microsites with an entirely different community makeup—wetlands, for example—may be embedded within an otherwise uniform type. Certain key species of a forest cover type may be present in one location but absent in

Most Michigan forests currently are in the early to mid-stages of secondary succession.

another one just down the road. **Exotic invasives** (aggressive non-native plants or animals) may overwhelm native vegetation, in certain cases creating a new deviation on an existing community type. We must always keep in mind that variation and change are hallmarks of the natural world.

Furthermore, disturbances and secondary succession immensely complicate the typing of forests. A distinct forest community today may slowly evolve into something very different in tens or hundreds of years through the process of secondary succession. Likewise, an existing forest type may experience a disturbance—e.g., a severe windstorm, wildfire, or logging—and the recovering forest community may possess only some of the attributes of the former community type, although successionally it may be headed in that direction. Land cleared for agriculture for many years, then abandoned, may succeed

back to a community unlike its ancestor on that site. Acid precipitation and global climate change have become long-term modifiers of forest cover. Therefore, the forest that exists today in any given place should be viewed as a fleeting phase; sooner or later it will change to a different community. And sometime during the change, it may not conveniently fit into a given community type.

Finally, Michigan is the Great Lakes state, and the lakes contain many islands and archipelagoes. Because they are surrounded by water, often have distinct climates, sometimes are quite remote, and have varied disturbance histories, island communities may be quite different from their mainland counterparts. Plant and animal species found on the mainland may be absent from an outlying island. Certain plant or animal species may be present on one island but absent from one close by. For example, white pine occurs on Beaver Island and three of the surrounding large islands but is absent on all other islands in the Beaver Island Archipelago, even though suitable habitats exist on them. White-tailed deer occur on North Manitou Island but not on South Manitou, a situation with great ecological significance. Islands, therefore, always should be viewed as unique situations.

Any treatment of a subject like this is idiomatic, and mine is no different. The trees, other plants, and animals that inhabit Michigan can occur together in an almost infinite array of combinations and permutations. By necessity, forest typing requires that boundaries and limits be established within this infinitude, sometimes quite arbitrarily. Furthermore, each person or group who attempts a forest type classification has a different perspective on where these boundaries are established. "Lumpers" look for wide boundaries defined by common traits and accept a considerable range of variation within them. "Splitters," on the other hand, attempt to sort natural variation out into a large number of tightly defined units. Examples of the latter approach include the ecological classification system for the Huron-Manistee

Trilliums are a much-loved spring wildflower.

National Forests by Cleland et al. (1993) and the U.S. National Vegetation Classification *Plant Communities of the Midwest* (Faber-Langendoen 2001). Both camps have adherents, and neither is right or wrong—there is a place for both. In the former case, simplicity may gloss over variability; in the latter case, the complexity of a large number of units leads to a difficult and unwieldy classification for the beginner. I chose ground that lies somewhere between these two extremes, although my tendency is to lump when possible.

Forest community types in this book

The community types I describe represent the average condition of mature forests that have not been heavily logged in a selective way (**high graded**) or otherwise greatly altered by human activities. Variation should be expected, although certain common denominators usually are present. The absence of certain species where they "should be" and the presence of species where they "shouldn't," therefore, need not cause concern. Time of year also is extremely important for ground layer plants—every flower has its season. So don't bother to look for blooming jack-in-the-pulpit in the fall (although the brilliant red fruit is easily spotted) or purple aster flowers in the spring.

The 23 types I describe are based on the major habitats they occupy. Spatially transitional communities are not described but may be inferred to share certain characteristics of the abutting types. Transition communities may be very narrow or absent (e.g., a pine plantation abutting a dry-mesic oak forest along a section line) or quite broad (e.g., a cedar swamp habitat gradually rising to a mesic northern hardwood forest). In other cases, the transition may be hardly noticeable if one is not looking for it (e.g., a dry-mesic oak forest in a draw morphing to a dry oak forest on a sandy hill).

I have drawn heavily upon the draft list and descriptions of natural communities and the very thoroughgoing community abstracts compiled by the Michigan Natural Features Inventory and posted on its Web site (www.msue.msu.edu/mnfi). I have modified their list by combining certain communities and adding successional forests that arose following major disturbances and forests of human origin. The treatments of forest community

classification by Barnes and Wagner (2004), McCann (1991), Cleland et al. (1993), Albert (1995), and Faber-Langendoen (2001) also were very helpful in developing this compilation. Useful information was obtained on wetland plants from Chadde (1998), on orchids from Case (1987), and on ferns from Billington (1952). My authority for plant names and their habitat associations is the three-volume *Michigan Flora* by Edward G. Voss (1972, 1985, 1996), an incredible resource for anyone interested in higher plants. Latin binomials of plants that I listed by common name are found on pages 28-30 (trees) and 153-158. Data on the area occupied by major forest types as of the last comprehensive state inventory in 1993 are from Leatherberry and Spencer (1996). I took the prehistoric

Cut-leaved toothwort, best seen up close.

and current extent of rare forest types from Michigan Natural Features Inventory community abstracts. Other references to certain types are cited in the text.

Using this guide

Types are organized into three categories — I. wetland, II. closed-canopy upland, and III. open-canopy upland—with southern communities described first, then northern communities. After a short description of the habitat, I list the signature overstory trees and some of their tree associates. Lists of understory woody plants, herbs, orchids, ferns, grasses, and sedges follow, but they are less inclusive and are not meant to be diagnostic. Rather, I have tried to assemble compilations of the plants that an observer is most likely to encounter or to recognize easily,

depending on the season of observation. Exotic invasives are followed by an asterisk. A rigorous examination of any community will uncover some understory ground flora species that I have omitted or some that should be there but are missing. There always are surprises in the natural world—that's half the fun of being out there!

The Michigan map included with each community type description colors the counties in which the type is most likely to be found. Some counties, naturally, will contain more of the type than others. The text that accompanies the maps provides more information on type distribution. The approximate locations of key viewing areas, where good examples of a particular community type can be visited, also are given in the text.

After the name of each community type, a code indicates how common it is across the state:

 = **widespread**; type very common in one or several regions or throughout the state, with many examples close at hand.

 = **local**; type confined to a specialized habitat in a particular region or regions of the state, yet not hard to find.

 = **rare**; type very uncommon and highly localized in the state, with very few examples.

This guide is meant to be used in conjunction with other field guides to plant and animal species identification (see pages 149 to 150). Consulting one or more of these guides can enhance the experience of Michigan forest watching. Keeping one's eyes open— with a bit of serendipity thrown in—can greatly enhance any foray into Michigan's marvelous forests. Expect the unexpected, and don't forget binoculars and insect repellent!

A serious forest watcher becomes engaged in her subject.

To identify a particular community type, ask the following questions:

- **What region of the state am I in? (See map on page 16.)**

- **Am I in a wetland habitat (river or stream bottom, wet depression, swamp, or bog) or a dry upland?**

- **Are there unique features of the habitat, such as rock outcrops or pavement, areas of open sand, stumps, or evidence of fire?**

- **Am I in a forest with a closed overhead canopy or are the trees scattered or clumped within a prairie or meadow; i.e., a savanna?**

- **What are the most common tree species in the overstory?**

- **What are the most common understory trees, shrubs, and herbs?**

Remember to be sure that you are well inside a uniform forest community and not in a transition area where two communities mix. Also be careful in mature early-successional forests that are shifting to a more stable late-successional community (e.g., aspen succeeding to boreal conifers or northern dry-mesic oak succeeding to white pine).

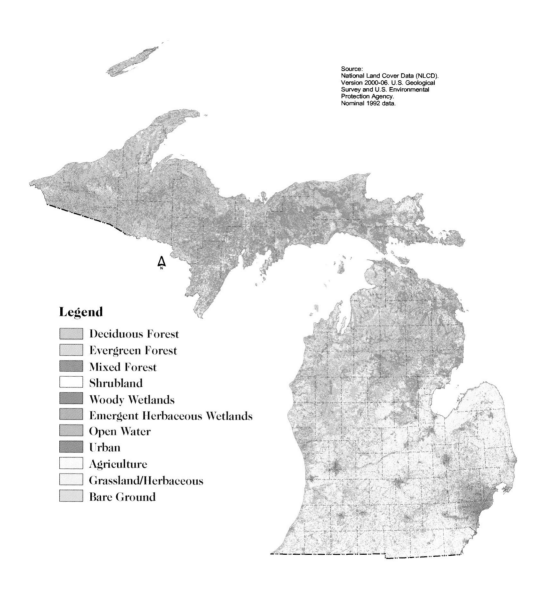

Source:
National Land Cover Data (NLCD).
Version 2000-06. U.S. Geological
Survey and U.S. Environmental
Protection Agency.
Nominal 1992 data.

Legend

- Deciduous Forest
- Evergreen Forest
- Mixed Forest
- Shrubland
- Woody Wetlands
- Emergent Herbaceous Wetlands
- Open Water
- Urban
- Agriculture
- Grassland/Herbaceous
- Bare Ground

Generalized map of Michigan's current vegetation.

✔ Checklist of Michigan Forest Community Types

✔ Checklist of Trees Native to Michigan*

Common name	Latin name
Gymnosperms (Conifers)	
Eastern white pine	*Pinus strobus*
Red pine (Norway pine)	*Pinus resinosa*
Jack pine	*Pinus banksiana*
White spruce	*Picea glauca*
Black spruce	*Picea mariana*
Balsam fir	*Abies balsamea*
Eastern hemlock	*Tsuga canadensis*
Tamarack (eastern larch)	*Larix laricina*
Northern white cedar	*Thuja occidentalis*
Eastern red cedar	*Juniperus virginiana*
Angiosperms (Deciduous hardwoods)	
Black willow	*Salix nigra*
Peachleaf willow	*Salix amygdaloides*
Balsam poplar	*Populus balsamifera*
Eastern cottonwood	*Populus deltoides*
Swamp cotton wood (E)**	*Populus heterophylla*
Bigtooth aspen	*Populus grandidentata*
Quaking aspen	*Populus tremuloides*

Common name	Latin name
Yellow birch	*Betula alleghaniensis*
Paper birch	*Betula papyrifera*
American beech	*Fagus grandifolia*
White oak group:	
White oak	*Quercus alba*
Swamp white oak	*Quercus bicolor*
Bur oak	*Quercus macrocarpa*
Chinkapin oak	*Quercus muehlenbergii*
Red oak group:	
Red oak	*Quercus rubra*
Scarlet oak	*Quercus coccinea*
Shumard oak	*Quercus shumardii*
Northern pin oak (Hill's oak)	*Quercus ellipsoidalis*
Pin oak	*Quercus palustris*
Black oak	*Quercus velutina*
Shingle oak	*Quercus imbricaria*
American chestnut (E)**	*Castanea dentata*
Black walnut	*Juglans nigra*
Butternut	*Juglans cinerea*
Bitternut hickory	*Carya cordiformis*
Pignut hickory	*Carya glabra*

✔ Checklist of Trees Native to Michigan*

Common name	Latin name
❑ Shellbark hickory	*Carya laciniosa*
❑ Shagbark hickory	*Carya ovata*
❑ Sugar maple	*Acer saccharum*
❑ Black maple	*Acer nigrum*
❑ Red maple	*Acer rubrum*
❑ Silver maple	*Acer saccharinum*
❑ Boxelder	*Acer negundo*
❑ White ash	*Fraxinus americana*
❑ Black ash	*Fraxinus nigra*
❑ Green ash (red ash)	*Fraxinus pennsylvanica*
❑ Blue ash	*Fraxinus quadrangulata*
❑ Pumpkin ash (T)**	*Fraxinus profunda*
❑ Basswood	*Tilia americana*
❑ Yellow poplar (tulip poplar)	*Liriodendron tulipifera*
❑ Black cherry	*Prunus serotina*
❑ American elm	*Ulmus americana*
❑ Slippery elm	*Ulmus rubra*
❑ Rock elm	*Ulmus thomasii*
❑ Hackberry	*Celtis occidentalis*
❑ Ohio buckeye	*Aesculus glabra*
❑ Honey locust	*Gleditsia triacanthos*
❑ Kentucky coffee tree	*Gymnocladus dioicus*
❑ Black gum	*Nyssa sylvatica var. sylvatica*

Common name	Latin name
❑ Sycamore	*Platanus occidentalis*
❑ Sassafras	*Sassafras albidum*
❑ Red mulberry	*Morus rubra*

Small hardwood trees and large shrubs

Common name	Latin name
❑ Pussy willow	*Salix discolor*
❑ Shining willow	*Salix lucida*
❑ Bog birch	*Betula pumila*
❑ Blue beech (musclewood)	*Carpinus caroliniana*
❑ Hop hornbeam (ironwood)	*Ostrya virginiana*
❑ Speckled alder	*Alnus rugosa*
❑ Dwarf chinkapin oak	*Quercus prinoides*
❑ Striped maple	*Acer pensylvanicum*
❑ Mountain maple	*Acer spicatum*
❑ Pin cherry	*Prunus pennsylvanica*
❑ Choke cherry	*Prunus virginiana*
❑ Wild plum	*Prunus americana*
❑ Canada plum	*Prunus nigra*
❑ Wild crabapple	*Malus coronaria*
❑ Juneberries (serviceberries)	*Amelanchier* spp.
❑ Hawthorns	*Crataegus* spp.
❑ American mountain ash	*Sorbus americana*

✔ Checklist of Trees Native to Michigan*

Common name	Latin name
❑ Showy mountain ash	*Sorbus decora*
❑ Flowering dogwood	*Cornus florida*
❑ Alternate-leaf dogwood	*Cornus alternifolia*
❑ Pawpaw	*Asimina triloba*
❑ Redbud	*Cercis canadensis*
❑ Witch hazel	*Hamamelis virginiana*
❑ Dwarf hackberry	*Celtis tenufolia*
❑ Nannyberry	*Viburnum lentago*
❑ Hoptree	*Ptelea trifoliata*

* For a complete description of the characteristics of these trees, see Barnes and Wagner (2004), Smith (1995), Petrides (1998), Tekiela (2002), or Voss (1972, 1985, 1996).

** E = endangered and T = threatened species protected under the Endangered Species Act of Michigan (Part 365, P.A. 451, 1994). See the Michigan Natural Features Inventory Web site (www.msue.msu.edu/mnfi) for a complete listing of the state's rare plants. Currently 51 species are endangered and 210 are threatened, in total nearly 15 percent of the state's native flora.

The glacial landforms of Michigan, combined with normally abundant rainfall, have produced an abundance of hydric (wet) habitats. Many of these habitats support closed- or open-canopy forests. Hydric habitats are especially common in the southern Lower Peninsula and eastern Upper Peninsula (regions I and III), although by no means are they limited to these areas. Hydric habitats result from poor internal soil drainage (e.g., former Great Lake beds, filled ponds [kettles] and lakes, depressions embedded in upland habitats, or valley bottoms); the high water tables adjacent to streams, rivers, ponds, and lakes; or a combination of both. Surface soils may be mineral or organic (muck or peat). Often hydric habitats have a distinct seasonality—water may stand or flow from early spring through midsummer, followed by a dry period that extends into the fall. Soils saturated with water are anoxic (deficient in oxygen), which is stressful to plants, especially if the water is stagnant. The plants that inhabit wetland communities, therefore, are uniquely adapted to cope with this stress. Many wetland plants can successfully compete only in hydric environments, and their distribution is limited to such places. Certain other wetland species are more cosmopolitan in their habitat tolerances, and they also successfully compete on uplands.

Wetlands are protected under Section 404 of the federal Clean Water Act of 1972 and Part 303 of the Michigan Natural Resources and Environmental Protection Act of 1994 (P.A. 451). These acts regulate the discharge of pollutants into wetlands, the building of dams and levees, infrastructure development, and the draining of wetlands for farming, forestry, or other purposes. Thus, compared with upland forests, wetlands enjoy some legislative buffering from destructive human activities.

 = **widespread**; type very common in one or several regions or throughout the state, with many examples close at hand.

 = **local**; type confined to a specialized habitat in a particular region or regions of the state, yet not hard to find.

 = **rare**; type very uncommon and highly localized in the state, with very few examples.

Habitat

The southern Lower Peninsula (Region I) contains about 30 major rivers and their tributaries, plus numerous short streams that drain directly to the Great Lakes (Sommers 1977). Their floodplains are home to this forest type. Additionally, extensive areas of poorly drained former lake bed that are seasonally inundated extend inland for considerable distances from Saginaw Bay, Lake St. Clair, and Lake Erie. Countless wet depressions also dot the landscape of this region. It is no wonder that early European explorers described this part of the state as a mosquito-infested swamp. Ditching and tiling by local drainage districts and filling by developers, however, has substantially reduced the area of wetland, and this trend continues. Nonetheless, hydric habitats still abound.

The soils of forested wetlands extend over a wide range of textures, from sand to clay, but all are poorly drained with neutral to slightly acid pH. Because root systems in these frequently saturated soils are shallow, tree windfalls are common. Hydric swamp or floodplain habitats may be sharply defined by banks,

terraces, or sloughs, or they may gradually rise to an adjoining upland. Transition habitats can be complex, containing a mixture of species adapted to both wetlands and uplands.

Signature trees

The following species are nearly always present in some combination, although elms have been greatly reduced in importance and stature by Dutch elm disease:

- **Silver maple**
- **Red maple**
- **Green ash**
- **Black ash** (swamp species)
- **American elm**
- **Eastern cottonwood**
- **Black willow** (very tolerant of saturated soils and frequently grows at water's edge)

Other trees

- Quaking aspen
- Peachleaf willow
- Boxelder
- Swamp white oak
- Bur oak
- Slippery elm
- Yellow birch

Tree diversity in this type generally declines from south to north because many tree species reach the northern limit of their natural range in southern Michigan. North of the latitude of Lansing (42 degrees), most of these southern species begin to drop out.

Seasonally wet silver maple woodland.

Thus floodplains, other wetlands, and their transition habitats in the lower two tiers of counties may contain, in addition to the species listed above:

- Butternut
- Black walnut
- Ohio buckeye
- Sycamore
- Hackberry
- Pin oak
- Shagbark hickory
- Bitternut hickory
- Black gum
- Blue ash
- Honey locust
- Kentucky coffee tree
- Red mulberry
- Swamp cottonwood

Buttonbush.

Associated plants

Sparsely wooded wetlands, openings, and stream banks will typically have a dense, rich complement of woody shrubs, whereas in dense forests where standing water persists, there may be few. Some of the more common shrubs and vines, listed in descending order of their tolerance for standing water, include:

- Bebb willow
- Pussy willow
- Sandbar willow
- Buttonbush
- Northern prickly ash
- Michigan holly (winterberry)
- Spicebush
- Pale dogwood

- Gray dogwood
- Red-osier dogwood
- Common elderberry
- Pawpaw
- Wild black currant
- Poison ivy
- Virginia creeper
- Riverbank grape

The ground cover in floodplains and swamps is typically quite variable. Where water stands for long periods, herb vegetation is sparse. In areas that dry out quickly or on wetland-upland transition sites, herbs can form a dense, waist-high cover. Although a large number of herbs could grow in wetlands and transition sites (e.g., see Type 6), only a few will be mentioned:

Prickly ash.

Marsh marigold.

Giant ragweed.

- Wood nettle
- Stinging nettle
- Spotted touch-me-not (jewelweed)
- Clearweed
- Wood sage
- Marsh marigold
- Jerusalem artichoke
- Panicled aster
- Rough-leaved goldenrod
- Virginia cowslip
- Giant ragweed
- Swamp milkweed
- Fringed loosestrife
- Moneywort
- Garlic mustard*
- Skunk cabbage
- Southern blue flag iris
- Wild ryegrass
- Wood reed grass
- White grass
- Fowl manna grass

Woodnettle.

Exotic (non-native)

Distribution and status

Wetland forest communities are very common throughout southern Michigan (more than 1.6 million acres); a short drive from any location will reveal several examples. Occasional occurrences of this type also may be found in Region II—e.g., the middle reaches of the Muskegon River—or along the Menominee River in the extreme southern Upper Peninsula (Region III). Although some of the land formerly occupied by this type has been drained for agriculture and filled for urban development (e.g., much of the greater Detroit area), overall wetland forests are in no immediate danger.

Key viewing areas

- Indian Springs Metropark (Oakland County northwest of Pontiac).
- Kalamazoo River floodplain, Allegan State Game Area (Allegan County west of Allegan).
- Waterloo State Recreation Area (Jackson and Washtenaw counties northeast of Jackson).
- Nan Weston Nature Preserve at Sharon Hollow, Michigan Nature Conservancy (Washtenaw County southwest of Chelsea).
- Red Cedar River floodplain, Harris Nature Center (Ingham County southeast of Okemos).
- Shiawassee National Wildlife Refuge and Shiawassee River State Game Area (Saginaw County southwest of Saginaw).

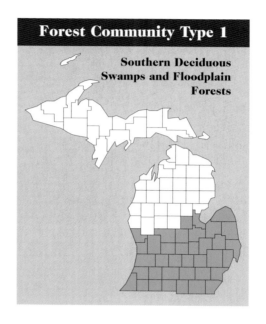

Forest Community Type 1

Southern Deciduous Swamps and Floodplain Forests

Uses and management

Most tree species in this type have low timber value. Nonetheless, some timber in deciduous wetland forests is managed and harvested, provided necessary permits are secured and best management practices (BMP) are followed. Logging typically is limited to winter and late summer because of accessibility constraints. Some firewood cutting also occurs. Trapping and hunting of waterfowl, woodcock, ruffed grouse, and deer are widely practiced in many of these communities. The best use of deciduous wetland forests is the protection of the water resources that produce them and the unique biota associated with them.

Habitat

These unique forested peatlands can be found in depressions, stream headwaters, and drainageways throughout southern Michigan. Underlying muck soils are neutral in pH, but surface peat layers are acidic. Their hydrology is maintained by calcareous groundwater. Disturbance agents include windthrow, fire, beaver flooding, and insect outbreaks. Never extensive, they contrast with the pervading deciduous upland and wetland communities. Ecologically, these swamps are islands set in a matrix of urban development, deciduous woodlands, and agricultural fields.

Signature tree

One deciduous conifer (the only one native to Michigan) dominates this forest type:

- **Tamarack**

Other trees

- Red maple
- Silver maple
- Yellow birch
- Black ash
- American elm
- Quaking aspen
- Swamp white oak
- Ohio buckeye

Tamarack's autumn gold.

- Northern white cedar (occasionally)
- White pine (rarely)
- Black spruce (rarely)

Associated plants

The shrub and vine component of this community is abundant and diverse because of the open tamarack canopy:

- Poison sumac
- Nannyberry
- Bog birch
- Alder-leaved buckthorn
- Glossy buckthorn*
- Pussy willow
- Spicebush
- Mountain holly
- Michigan holly
- Gray dogwood
- Pale dogwood

Poison sumac

38

Boneset.

- Golden ragwort
- Marsh bellflower
- Tufted loosestrife
- Bedstraws
- Wild lily-of-the-valley
- Starflower
- Clearweed
- Pitcher plant
- Sundews
- Skunk cabbage
- Wapato (arrowhead)
- Showy lady slipper orchid
- Arethusa orchid
- White-fringed orchid
- Grass-pink orchid
- Cattail
- Sedges
- Spinulose wood fern

- Hazelnut
- Shrubby cinquefoil
- Highbush blueberry
- Swamp gooseberry
- Black chokeberry
- Poison ivy
- Virginia creeper

Herbs are distinctive in these peatlands:
- Marsh marigold
- Water hemlock
- False nettle
- Spotted touch-me-not
- Tickseed sunflower
- Swamp aster
- Rough-leaved goldenrod
- Boneset
- Joe Pye weed
- Swamp thistle

Swamp thistle.

- Sensitive fern
- Royal fern
- Marsh shield fern

* Exotic (non-native)

Distribution and status

Although not common, relict conifer swamps are scattered across the southern Lower Peninsula. Because the dominant trees are not economically important, they are in no danger from human overexploitation. Nonetheless, drainage and disruption of local hydrology by human activities are threats, and collectors have depleted populations of several orchids.

Key viewing areas

- Kensington Metropark (Oakland County east of Brighton).

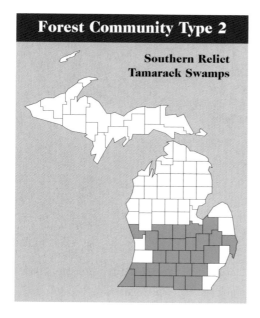

Wapato (arrowhead).

- Highland State Recreation Area (Oakland County west of Pontiac).

- Pinckney and Waterloo state recreation areas (Jackson and Washtenaw counties north and west of Chelsea).

- Rose Lake Wildlife Research Area (Clinton and Shiawassee counties northeast of Lansing).

- Binder Park Zoo (Calhoun County south of Battle Creek).

Uses and management

These wetlands are not managed for timber or other purposes except for some occasional firewood cutting (tamarack wood is the heaviest among Michigan conifers). Orchid collecting does occur, but it is illegal. These singular southern forests are best left alone for wetland protection and to provide valuable habitat for resident plants and animals.

Forest Community Type 2

Southern Relict
Tamarack Swamps

Habitat

Essentially a northern variation of southern deciduous swamps (Type 1), these poorly drained, seasonally inundated communities are found on floodplains, glacial lake plains, and morainal stream headwaters. Slightly acid to neutral soils are sandy to sandy loam in texture or shallow (occasionally deep) muck over a mineral substrate. As in most wetland forests, windthrow of large trees is common because rooting depth is restricted by seasonally anoxic conditions. Bleached elm skeletons, victims of Dutch elm disease, also are common.

Signature trees

Hardwoods dominate these swamps, sometimes to the nearly complete exclusion of conifers:

- **Black ash**
- **Green ash**
- **White ash**
- **Yellow birch**
- **American elm**

- **Red maple**
- **Basswood**
- **Paper birch**
- **Balsam poplar**
- **Quaking aspen**

Other trees

Several conifers may be found in these wetlands, but they are always mixed with hardwoods:

- Balsam fir
- Tamarack
- Northern white cedar
- White pine
- Hemlock

Associated plants

Because of seasonal flooding, barren areas in the understory are common. In drier places, however, the small tree-shrub layer can be quite rich:

- Canadian yew
- Juneberries
- Willows
- High-bush cranberry
- Wild raisin
- Dwarf raspberry
- Michigan holly
- Mountain holly

Black ash often dominates these communities.

Rough-leaved goldenrod.

Some important herbs include:

- Creeping snowberry
- Wood nettle
- Stinging nettle
- Water-horehound
- Skunk cabbage
- Marsh marigold
- Golden ragwort
- Rough-leaved goldenrod
- Enchanter's nightshade
- Mad-dog skullcap
- Goldthread
- Marsh skullcap
- Wild mint
- Spotted touch-me-not
- Swamp milkweed
- Joe Pye weed

- Bedstraws
- Smooth white violet
- Wild lily-of-the-valley
- Blue flag iris
- Wapato
- Sedges
- Shield fern
- Maidenhair fern
- Cinnamon fern
- Sphagnum moss

Distribution and status

This is a common wetland type characteristic of the Region I-II transition zone and northward through the northern Lower Peninsula (approximately 500,000 acres) and the Upper Peninsula (approximately 350,000 acres). Because it is so widespread, of little economic importance, and not

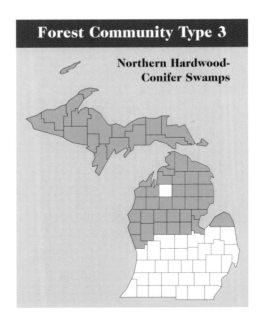

Forest Community Type 3

Northern Hardwood-Conifer Swamps

Joe Pye weed.

under development pressure, its status is secure. Although some of these wetlands were ditched and drained in the past, less of that is likely in the future.

Key viewing areas

• Jordan River Valley, Gaylord State Forest Management Unit (Antrim County north of Mancelona).

• Pigeon River Country State Forest (Cheboygan and Otsego counties northeast of Gaylord).

• Douglas Lake area, University of Michigan Biological Station (Emmet County northeast of Pellston).

• Wilderness State Park (Emmet County west of Mackinaw City).

Uses and management

Only a few trees in this type have substantial timber value (e.g., yellow birch, white cedar, white pine, and black ash for baskets). Nonetheless, selective cutting of these and other species has been practiced, usually during the late-summer dry season or the winter freeze-up. This practice is likely to continue on a local basis. Clear-cutting of this or any other wetland type should be done with caution because complete removal of tree cover can cause water tables to rise to the surface for an abnormally long period and inhibit tree reproduction. Like other forested wetlands, hardwood-conifer swamps provide valuable habitat for many wildlife species.

Cinnamon fern.

Michigan holly.

Habitat

Found along streams and drainage-ways; adjacent to inland lakes; in abandoned embayments and interdunal swales along the Great Lakes; and also in depressions in outwash plains, till plains, and lake plains, these forests are a defining feature of northern Michigan landscapes. Organic muck or peat soils are acid at the surface, but subsurface soil layers may be neutral or slightly alkaline in pH, especially where they overlie limestone or dolomitic bedrock (e.g., along the Lake Huron shore in the northeastern Lower Peninsula and throughout the eastern Upper Peninsula). Structure and composition of these forests are strongly influenced by a constant flow of cold, mineral-rich groundwater through the soil. Trees tend to be very shallow rooted because of saturated soils. Wind, therefore, is the major disturbance, typically creating an untidy tangle of uprooted and leaning trees. Fires are rare, occurring only after prolonged periods of drought. These swamps are one of the most floristically diverse forest communities in Michigan.

Signature trees

One singular conifer, often occurring in nearly pure stands, defines this type:

- **Northern white cedar**

Another unique conifer usually is present, sometimes dominating the cedar:

- **Tamarack**

Other trees

- White pine
- White spruce
- Black spruce
- Balsam fir (often in the understory)
- Hemlock
- Red maple
- Black ash
- Paper birch
- Yellow birch
- American elm
- Quaking aspen
- Balsam poplar

Associated plants

Many shrubs can be found in these wetlands:

- Speckled alder
- Mountain alder
- Bog birch
- Michigan holly
- Mountain holly
- Common elderberry
- American mountain ash
- Mountain maple

Shrubby cinquefoil.

- Red-osier dogwood
- Pale dogwood
- Alternate-leaved dogwood
- Shrubby cinquefoil
- Huckleberry
- Velvetleaf blueberry
- Labrador tea
- Leatherleaf
- Fly honeysuckle
- Swamp fly honeysuckle
- Wild black currant
- Swamp black currant
- Swamp red currant

Canada yew once was common in the understory, but it has been largely extirpated from this type by excessive deer browsing.

Characteristic plants in the herb layer include:

- Bunchberry
- Creeping snowberry
- Goldthread
- Starflower
- Twin flower
- One-flowered pyrola
- Grass of Parnassus
- Spotted touch-me-not
- Wild sarsaparilla
- Small enchanter's nightshade
- Wild lily-of-the-valley
- Joe Pye weed
- New England aster
- Bedstraw
- Rattlesnake grass
- Fowl manna grass

Sensitive fern.

Grass of Parnassus.

- Cotton grass
- Sedges
- Maidenhair fern
- Lady fern
- Rattlesnake fern
- Spinulose woodfern
- Cinnamon fern
- Sensitive fern
- Showy lady slipper orchid
- Yellow lady slipper orchid
- Early coral root orchid
- Tall white bog orchid
- Tall northern bog orchid
- Sphagnum moss

Distribution and status

Cedar swamps occur mostly in northern Michigan (regions II, III, and IV), where they are very common. A few remnants do crop up in the southern part of the state. Total state area is approximately 1.35 million acres, with nearly half in the eastern Upper Peninsula. The future of this type, however, is clouded by the state's enormous deer herd. Young cedar regeneration is literally browsed to death by these animals, especially in winter yarding areas. Young swamp cedar stands, therefore, are rare. Many ecologists and foresters predict a decline in cedar acreage, with conversion to species not heavily browsed (e.g., tamarack or balsam fir) unless deer numbers can be controlled.

New England aster.

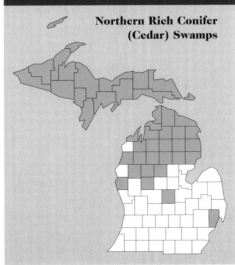

Forest Community Type 4

Northern Rich Conifer (Cedar) Swamps

Key viewing areas

- Stony Creek Metropark (Macomb County northeast of Rochester)— a southern remnant.

- Dead Stream Swamp, Cadillac State Forest Management Unit (Missaukee County northeast of Cadillac).

- Reese's Swamp, University of Michigan Biological Station (Emmet County northeast of Pellston).

- Grass Bay Nature Preserve (Cheboygan County east of Cheboygan)—access requires permission from The Nature Conservancy.

• Foley Creek Trail, Horseshoe Bay Wilderness Area, Hiawatha National Forest (Mackinac County north of St. Ignace).

• Upper Peninsula Tree Improvement Center, Michigan State University (Delta County west of Escanaba).

• Pictured Rocks National Lakeshore (Alger County northeast of Munising).

Cedar severely browsed by deer.

Uses and Management

Northern white cedar long has been prized for its wood, which is lightweight, easily split, and rot-resistant. Cedar still is harvested extensively for fence posts and rails, decking, cabin logs, canoe lumber, etc. Sustainable management for cedar revolves around reducing deer herds so that numbers are in balance with the habitats they

Jewelweed (spotted touch-me-not).

occupy. Only then will young cedar reproduction be able to grow into mature stands to replace trees that are harvested or die naturally. Time will tell if that goal is achievable, given hunter pressure on the Department of Natural Resources for more deer. Small clearcuts or strip timber harvests followed by prescribed fire to prepare a good seedbed have been successful. An uneven-aged management system also will work because cedar naturally self-perpetuates in gaps created by windthrown trees. Tamarack is used for pulpwood, pilings, and cabin logs. It usually will regenerate aggressively following harvests if seed sources are present.

Other than their timber values, cedar wetlands are prime regulators of local hydrology, a very important function. In addition, they provide very critical wildlife habitat—particularly during the winter—and they support a treasure of biological diversity.

Habitat

This type is found in poorly drained or undrained depressions and kettles in glacial outwash, till plains, and lake plains. Soils are organic and consist of deep, very acid, saturated peats devoid of groundwater influence. The result is an infertile and stressful soil environment. These forests mostly occupy former lakes and ponds that have filled in with undecomposed plant residues over the course of thousands of years. Often trees will form a ring of decreasing density around a shrub- and sphagnum-dominated floating wetland in the center of a former lake or pond. Periodic fires and insect outbreaks occur in these forested wetlands, and some have been drained, but generally they have been relatively free of direct human disturbances.

Tamarack is a common associate of black spruce.

Signature trees

Conifers dominate, with one species often forming pure stands (in muskegs, trees are scattered and stunted):

- **Black spruce**

Frequent associates include:

- **Tamarack**
- **Balsam fir**
- **Jack pine** (often on sandy hummocks or ridges)

Other trees

- White pine
- Northern white cedar

Associated plants

The deep, acid peats of conifer bogs and muskegs support several distinctive small trees and shrubs:

- Bog birch
- Speckled alder
- Leatherleaf
- Labrador tea
- Bog laurel
- Bog rosemary
- Velvetleaf blueberry
- Small cranberry
- Large cranberry
- Meadowsweet

Ground-layer plants are equally distinctive:

- False Solomon seal
- Bunchberry
- Twinflower
- Smooth white violet
- Pitcher plant
- Sundews
- Indian pipe
- Blue-bead lily
- Wild calla
- Cotton grass
- Beak rush
- Sedges

Meadowsweet (spiraea).

- Sphagnum moss (several species)
- Grass-pink orchid
- Heartleaf twayblade orchid
- Pink lady slipper orchid
- Green adder's mouth orchid
- Cinnamon fern

Distribution and status

These wetlands are found commonly in regions III and IV (Upper Peninsula), although they do occur in Region II and even Region I. In total they occupy approximately 465,000 acres and contribute greatly to the "wilderness" aspect of northern Michigan. Some of these communities were drained in the past to improve forest productivity. This forest community type is secure

Pitcher plant.

because it is inaccessible, very low in timber value, and protected by wetland laws. It will be a defining local feature of the northwoods for a long time to come.

Key viewing areas

- Waterloo State Recreation Area (Jackson County northeast of Jackson)—southernmost limit of this type.

- Lake Skegemog, Traverse City State Forest Management Unit (Kalkaska County northwest of Kalkaska).

Forest Community Type 5

Northern Conifer Bogs and Muskegs

Sphagnum mat under black spruce.

Indian pipe (white), Labrador tea, and sphagnum moss.

- Wilderness State Park (Emmet County west of Mackinaw City).

- Tahquamenon Falls State Park; vicinity of Betsy, Sheephead, and Clark lakes (Luce and Chippewa counties northeast of Newberry).

- Seney National Wildlife Refuge (Schoolcraft County northeast of Manistique).

Uses and management

Because trees grow so slowly in these wetlands and they are difficult to access, timber rarely is harvested from them. Like cedar swamps, northern conifer wetlands regulate local hydrology, and that is their most important function. In addition, they provide habitat for many northern birds and animals, and they are an intriguing part of the ecology of northern landscapes.

Leatherleaf and silvery bog rosemary.

The extensive uplands of Michigan are largely of glacial origin. They include hilly ice-contact features—moraines, kames, eskers, drumlins, and crevasse fillings—as well as flat or gently undulating till plains, outwash plains, and well-drained former lakebeds. Near the shore of Lake Michigan and in some inland areas, wind-shaped sand dunes also are a distinctive feature. In the highlands of the western Upper Peninsula, ancient bedrock forms prominent, mountainous ridges. Surface soils in mesic or wet-mesic habitats are medium- to heavy-textured (sandy loams to clay loams), and internal soil drainage is sufficient to prevent water from standing for any extended period.

Dry-mesic or xeric (very dry) habitats are typified by sandy or gravelly surface soils with rapid internal drainage. Plant water stress can quickly develop in these excessively drained habitats. The closed forests (i.e., those with a more or less continuous overstory tree canopy) that occupy these varied habitats are extremely diverse. Local differences in climate and history add their influence to habitat variation to create the state's fascinating and diverse mosaic of upland forest communities.

 = **widespread**; type very common in one or several regions or throughout the state, with many examples close at hand.

 = **local**; type confined to a specialized habitat in a particular region or regions of the state, yet not hard to find.

 = **rare**; type very uncommon and highly localized in the state, with very few examples.

Habitat

It doesn't get any better than mesic, especially southern mesic. Forests occupying these habitats are the most species-rich and productive in the state. Terrain—consisting of till plains, end moraines, and old lake plains—is level to rolling. Soils are deep, loamy, generally well-drained, and fertile. Within 10 to 20 miles of the Great Lakes, the humid climate also permits mesic forests to thrive on stabilized sand dunes. It is no wonder that much of the pre-European settlement mesic forest of southern Michigan was cleared for farming. Today, after a century and a half (more or less) of cultivation, these areas still are our most productive agricultural land. Straight-line winds are the major natural disturbance in mesic forests; in mature stands, uprooted or wind-snapped trees are common. Tornadoes and ice storms cause more extensive damage but are less common.

Signature trees

Mesic southern forests always contain one or both of our most tolerant hardwood species:

- **Sugar maple**
- **American beech**

Sugar maple — Michigan's most valuable tree.

Sugar maple usually dominates in the richest mesic habitats, whereas beech is better adapted to sandy soils or those with somewhat poor internal drainage. But it is common to find both species growing together. Seedlings and saplings of sugar maple usually predominate in the understory.

Other trees

Several other trees, which can become quite large, also may occupy a major part of the overstory but rarely establish in the understory of mature forests unless wind or logging opens a gap in the canopy:

- Red oak
- White oak
- Bur oak
- Chinquapin oak
- White ash
- Tulip poplar
- Basswood
- Black cherry
- Red maple
- Bitternut hickory
- Black walnut
- Sassafras
- White pine
- Hemlock (this and the preceding species occasionally near Lake Michigan and in the Region I-II transition zone)

Associated plants

The richness of mesic habitats is reflected in a high understory diversity. Small trees, shrubs, and vines may include:

- Blue beech
- Hop hornbeam
- Choke cherry

- Juneberries
- Pawpaw
- Prickly gooseberry
- Prickly ash
- Spicebush
- Red elderberry
- Maple-leaved viburnum
- Virginia creeper
- Poison ivy

Spring ephemerals are abundant in these forests, as are many other herbs, creating a colorful wildflower garden:

- Wild leek
- Wild ginger
- Common trillium
- Yellow trout lily (adder's tongue)
- Common blue violet
- Yellow violet
- Spring beauty
- Dutchman's breeches
- Cut-leaved toothwort

Large-flowered trillium.

Tall bellflower.

- Blue phlox
- Tall bellflower
- Enchanter's nightshade
- Anise root
- Mad-dog skullcap
- Wood nettle
- False rue anemone
- Wild geranium

Red elderberry.

- Pokeweed
- Blue cohosh
- Blue-stem goldenrod
- Beech drops
- Hairy Solomon seal
- False spikenard
- Showy orchis
- Fowl manna grass
- Wide-leaved sedge
- Lady fern

Distribution and status

Maple-beech forests are the most common forest type in southern Michigan. The largest area occurs in Van Buren, Calhoun, Allegan, Oakland, Kent, Barry, St. Clair, Ingham, and Sanilac counties, although extensive tracts are rare. Most of the land in southern Michigan that once supported this forest type has been converted to

Jack-in-the-pulpit above wild ginger.

agriculture—about 1.3 million fragmented acres remain. Farm woodlots are the major refuge for this type, although most have been heavily cut over. Because of the amazing vitality and reproductive power of the plants that make up these forests, those spared the ax or saw for a long period usually recover to a condition approaching what they were in pre-European settlement times, although some species may be lost.

Key viewing areas

- Stony Creek Metropark (Macomb County northeast of Rochester).
- Indian Springs Metropark (Oakland County northwest of Pontiac).
- Nan Weston Nature Preserve at Sharon Hollow, Michigan Nature

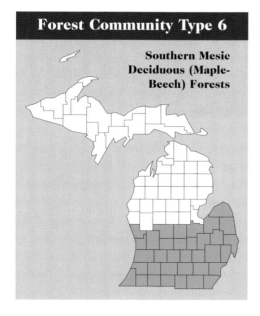

Forest Community Type 6

Southern Mesic Deciduous (Maple-Beech) Forests

Conservancy (Washtenaw County southwest of Chelsea).

• Toumey Woods, Sanford Woods, and Baker Woods, Michigan State University campus (Ingham County, East Lansing).

• Newton Woods, Fred Russ Forest (Cass County east of Dowagiac).

• Warren Woods State Park (Berrien County north of Three Oaks).

Uses and management

People have long benefited from the riches that this forest type provides. Many of its trees have high value for lumber and veneer, especially sugar maple, red and white oak, black cherry, black walnut, and tulip poplar. Sugar maple (and the closely related black maple) produce maple syrup and sup-

port a thriving small industry. In autumn the brilliant coloration of these forests draws people to country roads and trails for breathtaking views. And the diversity of plant and animal life found in these woods is a naturalist's dream.

Careful selective harvesting of a few mature trees per acre on a 10- to 15-year cycle mimics natural tree fall and can sustain a wood's basic uneven-aged structure. But this approach favors the very tolerant sugar maple and leads to an eventual decline in tree diversity. Small patch cuttings of one to several acres are necessary to allow less tolerant trees to reproduce and eventually reestablish themselves as members of the overstory canopy. Thinning frequently is used to favor the trees most valuable for timber and wildlife.

Lady fern.

Habitat

The hardwood forest community emblematic of much of southern Michigan, these forests occupy well-drained, moderately fertile habitats. They occupy mostly glacial ice-contact features—end moraines, kames, eskers, and till plains—so topography frequently is hilly or rolling. But these forests also can occur on flat, sandy lake plains. Near Lake Michigan they also grow in sand dunes. Soils are typically coarse-textured—mostly slightly acid sandy loams. Prior to European settlement, much of the land now in this forest type probably was oak openings—savanna communities maintained by annual fires set by native people. Some of this land was converted to agriculture by white settlers, and the most fertile land still is farmed. Other areas succeeded to closed forests when the fires ceased to burn or agriculture was abandoned. Surface fires can occur in this community, but wind and ice storms are the most common natural disturbances.

Signature trees

This is typically an oak-dominated forest type, with one or more of the following species always present:

- **Black oak**
- **White oak**
- **Red oak**

Other trees

Associated tree species may be present in small numbers or they may outnumber the oaks, especially if a stand has been selectively logged:

- Shagbark hickory
- Pignut hickory
- Sassafras
- Black cherry
- Red maple
- Bur oak
- White ash
- Basswood
- Black walnut
- Bigtooth aspen
- White pine (near Lake Michigan and in the Region I-II transition zone)

Associated plants

On very moist and rich dry-mesic habitats, a high understory diversity usually develops, including many of the species found in mesic hardwood forests (Type 6).

Blue beech (musclewood).

Poison ivy.

Mayapple.

Small trees, shrubs, and vines:

- Hop hornbeam (ironwood)
- Blue beech
- Witch hazel
- Eastern red cedar
- Flowering dogwood
- Juneberries
- Virginia creeper
- Common buckthorn*
- Greenbriar
- Common blackberry
- Summer grape
- Poison ivy
- Bracken fern

Herb layer

- False Solomon seal
- Bedstraw
- Red baneberry
- Black snakeroot
- Yellow violet
- Enchanter's nightshade
- May apple
- Garlic mustard*

- Canada bromegrass
- Sedge

* *Exotic (non-native)*

Distribution and status

Dry-mesic hardwoods are a common upland forest community in southern Michigan, covering about 700,000 acres. They can be found in every county in Region I, with the largest areas in Allegan, Kent, Barry, Jackson, Livingston, and Washtenaw counties. Virtually all of these woods were heavily cut over in the past, but most have regrown to a mature state. Because they are so widespread, their status is secure. Urban sprawl and unrestrained development, however, will continue to erode the extent of this forest type, especially in Oakland, Washtenaw, and Kent counties.

Forest Community Type 7

Southern Dry-Mesic Deciduous (Oak-Mixed Hardwood) Forests

Garlic mustard — a troublesome invasive.

Key viewing areas

- Kensington Metropark (Oakland County east of Brighton).

- Highland State Recreation Area (Oakland County west of Pontiac).

- Oakwoods and Willow metroparks (Wayne County south of Detroit Metro Airport).

- Dansville State Game Area (Ingham County southeast of Mason).

- Waterloo State Recreation Area (Jackson and Washtenaw counties northeast of Jackson).

- Yankee Springs State Recreation Area/State Park and Barry State Game Area (Barry County west of Hastings).

- Ross Preserve, Michigan Nature Conservancy (Van Buren County south of South Haven).

Uses and management

The importance of this forest type for timber and wildlife habitat can hardly be overstated. Oaks—particularly red and white oak—black cherry, and black walnut are among our finest hardwoods. Extraction of timber, therefore, always has been and will continue to be a major use of oak-dominated woodlands. Acorns are a major source of hard mast for deer, turkeys, blue jays, and many other animals, and hickory nuts and walnuts are vital to squirrel and mouse populations. Cherries provide soft mast for birds and other animals. In a good year, the late summer and fall bounty of these woodlands for wildlife is unsurpassed.

Like these hickories, trees in many dry-mesic woods are stump sprouts.

Foresters have long considered the management of oak forests problematic because oaks reproduce with difficulty. Acorns are eaten by many animals and birds, so little seed survives to germinate. Oaks do not thrive in shade and grow more slowly than competing species. Therefore, selective cutting of oaks discriminates against them and is not recommended. Small patch clearcuts or shelterwood harvests (i.e., removing about half of the overstory trees), along with plenty of soil disturbance and suppression of competing species with herbicides, seem to work best. Prescribed burning in regenerating stands also may be effective in suppressing oak competitors, which do not sprout back as vigorously as oaks after their tops are killed by a fire. But experience with this technique is limited. Thinning established stands to invigorate large mast-producing oaks and other species is a common practice.

Wild geranium.

Spring beauty.

8

Southern Dry Deciduous (Dry Oak) Forests

Habitat

This forest type occupies the driest habitats in southern Michigan—outwash plains, sand ridges in lake plains, and sand dunes. Soils are very well to excessively well-drained, acidic, and infertile. Soil textures mostly range from loamy sand to sandy loam. Before European settlement, many of the areas now occupied by closed forests of this type were oak openings or oak barrens main-tained by fire. Settlers' futile attempts at farming these low-productivity soils were soon abandoned. A distinction between this type and the former type may be difficult on transition habitats; e.g., where ice-contact topography abuts an area of outwash.

Signature trees

Tree diversity often is low in these sandy habitats. Two oaks predominate, both in the overstory and understory:

- **Black oak**
- **White oak**

Other trees

Associated canopy or subcanopy species usually are low in number:

- Shagbark hickory
- Pignut hickory
- Red maple
- Black cherry
- Sassafras
- Bigtooth aspen
- Hop hornbeam
- Scarlet oak
- Northern pin oak
- White pine (near Lake Michigan and in the Region I-II transition zone)

Wild lupine.

Associated plants

Shrubs and vines:

- Flowering dogwood
- Gray dogwood
- American hazelnut
- Witch hazel
- New Jersey tea
- Blueberries
- Virginia creeper
- Poison ivy
- Summer grape

Herb layer:

- Agrimony
- Hog peanut
- Beggars tick
- Bedstraw
- Wild geranium
- Stickseed
- Whorled loosestrife
- Wild lupine
- Indian pipe

Gray dogwood.

Flowering dogwood.

- False Solomon seal
- Solomon seal
- Pennsylvania sedge
- Christmas fern
- Rattlesnake fern

Distribution and status

These communities are not widely distributed and very local in occurrence. Exact acreage figures are not available because forest survey reporting does not distinguish this type from the dry-mesic oak type. Suburban and rural developments are the greatest threat to southern oak forests of any kind.

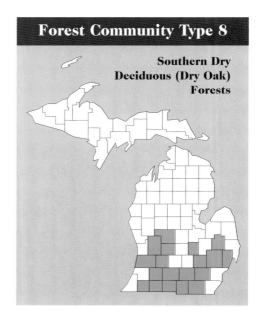

Forest Community Type 8

Southern Dry
Deciduous (Dry Oak)
Forests

False Solomon seal.

Key viewing areas

- Allegan State Game Area (Allegan County west of Allegan).

- Fort Custer State Park/Recreation Area (Kalamazoo County west of Battle Creek).

- Flat River State Game Area (Montcalm County southeast of Greenville).

Uses and management

Because these dry, infertile habitats are so unproductive, little use has been made of them, save some local timber harvesting or firewood cutting. They are best left alone to provide habitat for wildlife and protection for the highly erodible soils. In some places, attempts have been made to restore the oak barrens from which many of these stands originated by heavily thinning overstory trees and reintroducing periodic fires (see Type 18).

9

Northern Mesic Hardwood (Hemlock-Hardwood) Forests

Habitat

These communities are the northern extension of the southern mesic forest, with climate the distinguishing factor. Growing seasons become shorter, winter temperatures colder, and snowfall greater northward into the Lower Peninsula and westward into the Upper Peninsula. Nonetheless, these forests are rich and productive. They occur in fertile, well-drained mesic habitats on ice-contact, lake-plain, and sand dune features. Soils range from mostly acid loamy sands to loams. Although agriculture is not as pervasive in northern Michigan as it is in Region I, some of these communities were cleared for farming. Much of the cleared land remains in row crops, forage, or pasture today. Northern mesic hardwood communities rarely burn—in fact, some ecologists refer to them as "asbestos" forests. Wind is the major disturbance agent.

Signature trees

Because this community type occurs over a range of landforms and a large geographic area, its plant composition can vary considerably. Nonetheless, there are distinct commonalities. One hallmark tree usually always dominates, sometimes forming nearly pure stands:

- **Sugar maple**

Several other species also may be dominant on certain sites, but sugar maple usually is present in the overstory or understory:

- **American beech** (not present in Region IV)
- **Eastern hemlock** (especially in Region IV)

- **Red oak**
- **Basswood**
- **Yellow birch**

Other trees

Canopy associates are usually found in lower numbers than those above:

- Red maple
- White ash
- Black cherry
- Paper birch
- Bigtooth aspen
- Quaking aspen
- White pine
- White spruce
- Northern white cedar (sand dunes and calcareous soils)

Northern hardwoods in some form are found in regions II, III, and IV.

The signature conifers of this forest type—hemlock and white pine—were much more common in pre-European settlement times than they are today. Heavy cutting of these species during the late 19th and early 20th centuries, combined with repeated wildfires and—in recent decades—intense deer browsing, has reduced their importance.

Associated plants

On sandy soils, the understory in these communities may be quite bare, with low plant diversity. On richer sites, the understory is verdant and species-rich.

Maple-leaved viburnum.

Small trees and shrubs are common, least of all in the heavy shade in stands dominated by sugar maple:

- Striped maple
- Mountain maple
- Hop hornbeam (ironwood)
- Beaked hazelnut
- Alternate-leaved dogwood
- Fly honeysuckle
- Leatherwood
- Red elderberry
- Maple-leaved viburnum
- Prickly gooseberry
- Canadian yew (becoming rare because of intense deer browsing)

Wildflowers in the herb layer, especially spring ephemerals, produce a garden that rivals any of human design:

- Spring beauty
- Canada white violet

Herb Robert.

- Common blue violet
- Dutchman's breeches
- Squirrel corn
- Herb Robert
- Sharp-lobed hepatica
- Sweet cicely
- Miterwort
- Foamflower

73

Trout lily (adder's tongue).

- Blue cohosh
- Wild ginger
- Bellwort
- Enchanter's nightshade
- Bunchberry
- Bedstraw
- Starflower
- White baneberry
- Beech drops (beech stands only)
- Solomon seal
- Wild lily-of-the-valley
- Blue-bead lily
- Jack-in-the-pulpit
- Wild leek
- Trout lily (adder's tongue)
- Common trillium
- Nodding trillium
- Coral root orchid
- Sedges
- Spinulose wood fern
- Rattlesnake fern
- Maidenhair fern
- Lady fern
- Club mosses

Distribution and status

The most widely distributed forest type in northern Michigan at 5.9 million acres, mesic northern hardwoods are especially common in Otsego, Antrim, Kalkaska, Cheboygan, Emmet, Charlevoix, Benzie and Wexford counties in Region II; Alger and Luce counties in Region III; and all of the counties in Region IV (Dickinson the least). Although heavily cut over in the past, most of these communities have recovered well. White pine and hemlock, however, are not as common as they once were. Beech, though still common in regions II and III, is being killed in large numbers by the introduced beech bark disease. The future status, therefore, of this singular member of the northern hardwood community is in

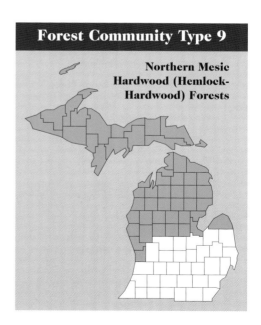

Forest Community Type 9

Northern Mesic Hardwood (Hemlock-Hardwood) Forests

White baneberry.

doubt. This type as a whole, however, is in no immediate danger, except very locally where development occurs.

Key viewing areas

- Manistee National Forest (Wexford County; west along M-55 between Cadillac and M-37).

- Jordan River Valley, Gaylord State Forest Management Unit (Antrim County west of Elmira).

- Sleeping Bear Dunes National Lakeshore (Benzie and Leelanau counties northwest of Traverse City).

- Tahquamenon Falls State Park (Luce and Chippewa counties northeast of Newberry).

- Pictured Rocks National Lakeshore (Alger County northeast of Munising).

- Sylvania Wilderness, Ottawa National Forest (Gogebic County southwest of Watersmeet).

- Porcupine Mountains State Park (Ontonagon County west of Ontonagon).

Beech (left) drops out in the western Upper Peninsula, but hemlock (right) becomes more common.

Uses and management

Like its southern counterpart, the mesic northern hardwood community is valuable for many reasons. Sugar maple is prized for its hard, cream-colored wood and the syrup made from its sap. Red oak and yellow birch also are among the finest hardwood timbers for lumber and veneer. In fact, most of the trees that grow in this type have commercial value. The display of fall color in these woods is unsurpassed in the northern landscape. Largely because of its extent and plant diversity, northern hardwood forests also are prime wildlife habitat.

Maidenhair fern.

Northern hardwoods can be managed under an uneven-aged system, where a few large trees per acre are periodically harvested, or an even-aged system employing small patch clearcuts or shelterwood harvests. Rotting stumps and large fallen logs provide microhabitats for yellow birch and hemlock seedling establishment, which is sparse without them. Thinning to increase diameter growth of the best trees can be used in either system. Uneven-aged management favors sugar maple, whereas the even-aged system promotes tree diversity. Applied carefully, both systems are sustainable.

Canada yew (dark green patches), once common, has become rare because of intense deer browsing.

Habitat

This extensive type is found on sandy outwash, lake bed, ice-contact, or dune features. Soils are mostly acid, moderately fertile, well-drained sands or loamy sands. Agriculture generally is not sustainable on these soils, so aside from some pastureland, areas once cleared for farming have reverted to forest, some of it oak-dominated. This type is largely an accident of human history. Prior to logging during the 19th and early 20th centuries, many northern areas now dominated by oaks were white and red pine forests, with oaks a minor overstory component, although they were common in the subcanopy or understory. The repeated wildfires that accompanied logging and settlement precluded the pines from reestablishing but favored the strong-sprouting oaks.

Signature trees

One or more oaks always are present as the major species in the overstory:

- **Red oak**
- **White oak** (regions I and II: rare in Region III and not in Region IV)

Flowering dogwood under an oak canopy near Lake Michigan.

- **Black oak** (Region I and the southwestern part of Region II only)
- **Northern pin oak** (localized in regions III and IV)

Other trees

- **White pine** (often in the understory)
- Red pine
- Jack pine
- Black cherry
- Red maple (seedlings often also present)
- Bigtooth aspen
- Quaking aspen

- Hemlock
- Balsam fir (usually subcanopy, especially near wetlands)

Associated plants

The small tree and shrub component may include:

- Juneberries
- Witch hazel
- Striped maple
- Mountain maple
- American hazelnut
- Beaked hazelnut
- Common blackberry
- Flowering dogwood (Region I and southwestern Region II only)

- Maple-leaf viburnum
- Gray dogwood
- Bush honeysuckle
- Huckleberry
- Blueberries
- Sweetfern

Many species can inhabit the herb layer, including:

- Wintergreen
- Bunchberry
- Trailing arbutus
- Large-leaved aster
- Pearly everlasting
- Twinflower
- Columbine
- Partridge berry
- Cow wheat
- Common milkweed
- Solomon seal

Cow wheat.

- Beggars tick
- Sarsaparilla
- Starflower
- Squawroot
- Wild lily-of-the-valley
- Blue-bead lily
- Pink lady slipper orchid
- Coral root orchid
- Indian pipe
- Pennsylvania sedge
- Poverty grass
- Rice grass
- Bracken fern
- Spinulose wood fern
- Ground pine

Columbine.

Distribution and status

The northern oak type occurs to a small extent near the Lake Michigan shore in Region I and in Chippewa and Marquette counties in the Upper Peninsula. Nearly 1.2 million acres, however, are found in Region II, primarily in Lake, Newaygo, Alcona, Roscommon, Crawford, Oscoda, Oceana, Mason, and Manistee counties. The status of this type, however, is tenuous. Oaks are not replacing themselves in undisturbed stands, and many are naturally reverting to white pine or more tolerant hardwoods such as red maple. Active management or wildfire, therefore, is necessary to perpetuate the oaks. In addition, many of the coun-

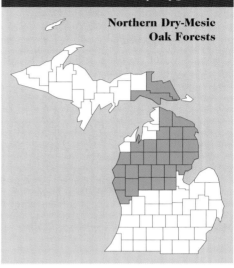

Forest Community Type 10

Northern Dry-Mesic Oak Forests

ties in Region II containing northern oak forests are being divided into small parcels and are under intense development pressure, which further jeopardizes the future of this type.

Key viewing areas

- White Cloud District, Manistee National Forest (Newaygo County in the vicinity of White Cloud).

- Coolbaugh Natural Area, Michigan Nature Conservancy (Newaygo County northeast of Newaygo).

- North Higgins Lake State Park (Roscommon and Crawford counties west of Roscommon).

- Interlochen State Park (Grand Traverse County southwest of Traverse City).

Pink lady slipper.

Star flower.

• Fife Lake Area, Traverse City State Forest Management Unit (Grand Traverse County east of Kingsley).

Uses and management

Red and white oaks produce some of the finest hardwood lumber and veneer. Black oak is less valuable. However, except on the richest, most productive sites in this type, trees generally are of low quality. Northern pin oak is considered inferior to its associates and, except for firewood, is little used. Anywhere oaks dominate the canopy is

State Archives of Michigan

After logging and repeated fires, many of Michigan's original pine forests succeeded to oak.

Witch hazel flowering in autumn after leaf fall.

valuable wildlife habitat, and these woods are no exception. They have long been considered prime territory for deer, squirrel, and turkey hunters.

Severe treatments are necessary to perpetuate dry-mesic oak forests. Clear-cutting mature stands, followed by stump sprouting, can be successful on sites that are not prone to late spring frosts. Where frost is a problem, leaving a partial overstory (shelterwood system) can protect young sprouts and seedlings. In either case, disturbed soil or prescribed fire is necessary to promote acorn germination. If natural oak reproduction is insufficient, seedlings can be planted, but results have been mixed. In either case, oak seedlings are severely browsed by deer. Release from competition by aggressive trees such as red maple also is necessary. Mature stands are sometimes thinned to promote diameter growth and acorn production of oaks.

Northern Dry-Mesic Pine Forests

Habitat

Same as that of Type 10, dry-mesic oak forests. Northern dry-mesic habitats once supported the magnificent old-growth white and red pine forests that made Michigan famous in the 19th century. This present-day type represents a second-growth reincarnation of the "cathedral pines" in areas where postlogging wildfires were not severe or repeated. In some places, however, the pine did not come back, nor did any other forest (see Type 23). Many people fondly associate these fragrant and stately forests with the north woods, and rightly so — they are a signature northern forest community. Both low-intensity surface and stand-replacing fires once occurred with regularity in this type, but they are infrequent today because of fire prevention and suppression measures.

Signature trees

The same species that occur in Type 10 also constitute this type, but now two pines dominate in variable mixtures:

- **Red (Norway) pine**
- **White pine**

Red pine is more common on dry sandy soils, whereas white pine will predominate on more mesic habitats.

Other trees

Numerous hardwood and conifer trees can be associated with the big pines:

Bracken fern.

Striped maple.

- White oak (rare in Region III and absent in Region IV)
- Black oak (region I and the southwestern part of Region II only)
- Northern pin oak (localized in regions III and IV)
- Red oak
- Red maple
- Black cherry
- Bigtooth aspen
- Quaking aspen
- Paper birch
- Jack pine
- Hemlock
- Balsam fir (usually subcanopy, near wetlands)
- White spruce (usually subcanopy in regions III and IV)

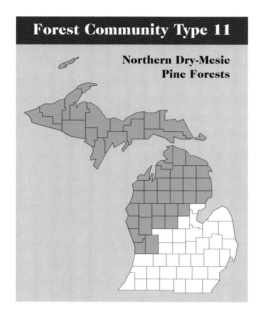

Forest Community Type 11

Northern Dry-Mesic Pine Forests

Associated plants

Same as those in Type 10. Young, dense pine forests usually have sparse shrub and herb layers. These layers usually become rich and verdant in older forests that have been thinned by natural mortality or silvicultural operations.

Distribution and status

Historically, red and white pine forests occurred in their greatest extent in Region II, the northern Lower Peninsula. At nearly 690,000 acres, this remains true today. Smaller though still extensive areas of this type can be found in Region III (226,000 acres) and, to a lesser extent, in Region IV (144,000 acres). Much of the red pine

acreage today, however, resulted from planting, especially in Region II (see Type 16). White pine is a more important component of the type in Region IV. Unless they are managed against, the area occupied by the big pines—especially white pine—will continue to increase in the future, largely at the expense of aspen-birch (Type 15) and dry-mesic oak (Type 10) forests.

Key viewing areas

• Mason Tract along the Au Sable River, Grayling State Forest Management Unit (Crawford County east of Roscommon).

Wild lily of the valley.

Club moss (Lycopodium).

- Hartwick Pines State Park (Crawford County north of Grayling)—old growth and second growth.

- Pigeon River State Forest Management Unit (Cheboygan and Otsego counties northeast of Gaylord).

- Wilderness State Park (Emmet County west of Mackinaw City).

- Tahquamenon Falls State Park (Luce and Chippewa counties northeast of Newberry).

- Pictured Rocks National Lakeshore (Alger County northeast of Munising).

Uses and management

Red and white pine have always been prime timber trees. Red pine wood is used for pulp, oriented-strand board, lumber (preservative-treated and untreated), utility poles, and cabin logs. White pine wood finds more use for interior applications—paneling, trim, flooring, and furniture. Timber harvesting, therefore, will continue unabated in this type in the future. These forests also are important for wildlife that use coniferous habitats.

The big pines usually are managed under an even-aged system. Mature stands can be clear-cut and replanted. But other, more benign options are available. Partial harvests of mature stands using a shelterwood system usually result in natural reproduction of the pines. When new seedlings are well established, the remaining overstory trees can be fully or partially removed. Small patch cuts also can be used to create or maintain an uneven-aged condition. Thinning immature stands to stimulate diameter growth of the best trees is widely practiced. Prescribed fires of low intensity will maintain the

Wintergreen.

open understory typical of pre-European settlement pine forests (page 82) and will promote herb diversity.

Pine woods benefit from low-intensity surface fires.

Habitat

This widely distributed community varies across the state depending on local landform, soil, and the geographic range of its component species. Yet there are many common features. Generally, these xeric sites support the least productive although in some ways the most interesting upland forests in the state. Occurring on flat or rolling sandy outwash and lake plains or on sand ridges in peatlands, soils are very acid, infertile, excessively drained, and droughty. Frosts can occur during the growing season. No other forest community is so frequently visited by major disturbances. Wildfires have always been common in these highly flammable forests. Prior to European settlement, fires burned every few decades, on the average, and they still burn regularly today. Outbreaks of jack pine budworm—a defoliating insect—also occur periodically, devastating large areas. Early white settlers—not bothering to ask native people, who knew better—tried to farm these habitats, but they soon came to grief. Most of the cleared land has reverted to forest.

The dry soil under jack pine supports a surprisingly verdant flora.

Signature trees

Tree diversity usually is low on these stressful habitats, with one singular species usually dominating, often in extensive pure stands:

- **Jack pine**

A common associate of jack pine, and often towering over it, this more regal conifer also can occur in nearly pure stands:

- **Red pine**

One scraggly hardwood commonly intermingles with the two pines:

- **Northern pin oak**

Other trees

- White pine
- Red oak
- Bigtooth aspen
- Quaking aspen
- Paper birch
- Red maple
- Black cherry
- Balsam fir (subcanopy of older stands, usually near wetlands)
- White spruce (subcanopy of older stands)

Northern pin oak readily hybridizes with red oak, creating a taxonomic tangle. Thus, identifying an individual member of the red oak group to the species level may be problematic.

Associated plants

The flora on these dry, infertile sites is surprisingly diverse.

Small trees and shrubs:

- Juneberries
- Choke cherry
- Prairie willow
- Sand cherry
- Sweetfern
- New Jersey tea
- Blueberries
- Huckleberry
- Northern dewberry
- Bush honeysuckle

Herb layer:

- Bearberry
- Wintergreen
- Birdfoot violet
- Large-leaved aster
- Arrow-leaved aster
- Spreading dogbane
- Wild lily-of-the-valley
- Cow wheat
- Canada hawkweed

Blueberry.

Bearberry.

- Orange hawkweed*
- Rattlesnake weed
- Spotted knapweed*
- Pipsissewa
- Hoary puccoon
- Trailing arbutus
- Wild strawberry
- Hair grass
- Rice grass
- Poverty grass
- Northern slender ladies'-tresses orchid
- Pennsylvania sedge
- Bracken fern
- Reindeer moss lichen

* *Exotic (non-native)*

Birdfoot violet.

91

Sweetfern.

Distribution and status

This type is widespread in northern Michigan. Region II contains the most jack pine forest (520,000 acres), with large areas in Crawford, Oscoda, Iosco, Ogemaw, and Kalkaska counties. Chippewa, Luce, and Schoolcraft counties in Region III and Marquette and Houghton counties in Region IV also contain extensive tracts of this type. Because they are so common, the status of these forests is secure. In Region II, additional protection is afforded young stands of jack pine because they are the only habitat for the endangered Kirtland's warbler. Federal law dictates that this habitat be protected and per-petuated. Nonetheless, some jack pine

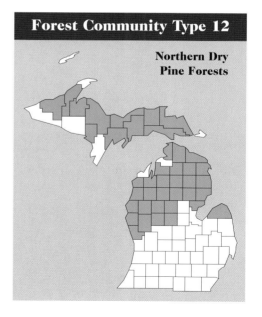

Forest Community Type 12

Northern Dry Pine Forests

Juneberry.

areas are being subdivided and developed, but any structure built in these forests is in considerable danger from wildfires. Homeowners in areas of dense jack pine should consult the World Wide Web Firewise home page (www.firewise.org) and take appropriate fire mitigation measures.

Key viewing areas

• Mio District, Huron National Forest, and Grayling and Roscommon state forest management units (Oscoda, Crawford, and Montmorency counties, centered on Mio).

• Raco Plains, Sault Ste. Marie District, Hiawatha National Forest (Chippewa County southwest of Sault Ste. Marie).

• Gwinn State Forest Management Unit (Marquette County between Gwinn and the K.I. Sawyer Airport).

• Baraga Plains, Baraga State Forest Management Unit (Baraga County west of Alberta).

Uses and management

Although these pine forests are relatively unproductive compared with more mesic forest types, the jack pine and red pine in them are widely used by the forest products industry—jack pine for pulpwood, lumber, and oriented-strand board (OSB), and red pine for pulp, OSB, lumber, poles, and cabin logs. Many birds and animals inhabit these forests, not the least of which is the endangered Kirtland's warbler.

Mature jack pine usually is clear-cut and replanted, with large oaks and red pine left standing to provide habitat diversity and visual interest. Extensive tracts have been managed this way for Kirtland's warbler habitat. The comeback of this bird in recent years has been largely due to this management strategy, along with eradication of parasitic cowbirds. In the future, more warbler habitat or now-rare pine barrens (see Type 19) may be created using prescribed fire.

Phil Huber

Wildfires always are a threat in jack pine forests.

Habitat

True northern boreal forests occupy huge areas in Canada and Alaska but are sparsely represented in Michigan. They typically occupy mesic to wet-mesic habitats along the shores of the Great Lakes, on islands (most notably Isle Royale and Drummond Island), and in a few local areas in the western Upper Peninsula. Soils vary widely in drainage (well-drained to somewhat poorly drained), pH (very acid to neutral) and texture (light sands to heavy clay loams). Landforms also are variable—sand dunes and lake beds to shallow soils over bedrock. Primary disturbance factors have been outbreaks of spruce budworm (a defoliating insect that actually prefers balsam fir), wildfires, and windstorms. Shallow rooting leads to many wind-thrown trees, especially those that have reached large size.

Bunchberry.

Signature trees

The tree component varies, depending on disturbance history and habitat. Two conifers usually dominate the overstory in stands not disturbed for long periods or the understory in early successional stands:

- **White spruce**
- **Balsam fir**

On sand dunes and soils over calcareous bedrock, another conifer dominates:

- **Northern white cedar**

After stand-replacing disturbances, two pioneer early-successional invaders usually take over:

- **Paper birch**
- **Quaking aspen**

Associated plants

Small trees and shrubs:

- Mountain maple
- American mountain ash
- Showy mountain ash
- Beaked hazelnut
- Fly honeysuckle

Herb layer:

- Bunchberry
- Red baneberry
- Sarsaparilla
- Twinflower
- Goldthread
- Sweet-scented bedstraw
- Starflower
- Wild lily-of-the-valley
- Blue-bead lily
- Dwarf lake iris
- Sedges
- Rattlesnake orchid

Royal fern.

- Ram's-head lady slipper orchid
- Royal fern
- Mosses and lichens

Forest Community Type 13

Boreal (Spruce-Fir)
Forests

Distribution and status

This type is very localized in the northern part of Region II and in regions III and IV; no acreage figures are available. Except for some limited extraction of white cedar, the type is rarely harvested for timber. The major threat to boreal communities is shoreline development, which in more accessible areas is rampant.

Key viewing areas

- Wilderness State Park (Emmet County west of Mackinaw City).

- Drummond Island (extreme eastern Chippewa County).

- Mary Macdonald Preserve at Horseshoe Harbor, Michigan Nature Conservancy (Keweenaw County east of Copper Harbor).

- Isle Royale National Park (Lake Superior northwest of Copper Harbor).

Uses and management

Aside from the unique wildlife habitat it provides and its recreational value, the major usefulness of this type is simply to be what it is, a minor though important part of Michigan's forest diversity. The best management of it is no management.

Michigan boreal forests occur along shorelines of the Great Lakes.

Showy mountain ash.

Habitat

A singular feature of Great Lakes shorelines, these wet-dry communities are a result of the slow rebounding of the land and recession of the lakes during the millennia following the retreat of the Wisconsin glacier. The undulating topography consists of sand ridges — former beachfront sand dunes — alternating with swales or interdunal wetlands. These communities are very apparent from the air, appearing as concentric rings radiating inland for up to 2 miles from bays along the present shoreline. Soils are generally acidic to neutral sands, well-drained on the ridges and poorly drained or undrained in the troughs. The wetland swales are maintained by the flow of surface streams or groundwater. The Michigan Natural Features Inventory (Albert and Comer 1999) classified dune forest-swale complexes into five subtypes on the basis of location and processes of beach ridge formation:

Southern dune forests often are dominated by oaks.

- Southern Lake Huron (tip of the Thumb).
- Northern Lake Huron-Lake Michigan low dune.
- Northern Lake Michigan high dune.
- Lake Superior low dune.
- Lake Superior high dune.

Characteristic plants

The communities occupying these complexes are highly variable and dependent on the area of the state and local conditions.

- Dry and dry-mesic conifer or hardwood forest communities (types 10, 11, or 12) usually occupy the sand ridges.
- Conifers or hardwood swamp communities (types 3, 4, or 5), wet meadows, fens, emergent marshes, or open sphagnum peat bogs are found in the interdunal troughs.

Distribution and status

Although very localized, these community complexes are common along Great Lakes embayments from the tip of the Thumb through regions II, III,

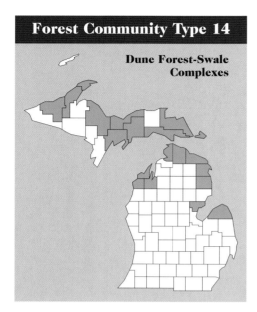

Forest Community Type 14

Dune Forest-Swale Complexes

and IV. Their status is fairly secure because the alternating wetlands limit to some extent accessibility for development and timber harvesting. Wetland legislation also protects them. Nonetheless, many of the complexes have been altered along highly valuable coastlines by road building, dredging, wetland filling, and residential development. The remaining intact complexes—mostly in northern Michigan—should be conserved because they are such a unique aspect of Great Lakes ecology.

A receding shoreline creates alternating dunes and swales.

Northern conifers rise above the swales in regions II, III, and IV.

Key viewing areas

- Albert E. Sleeper State Park and Huron County Nature Center Wilderness Arboretum (Huron County north of Bad Axe at the tip of the Thumb).

- Sturgeon Bay, Wilderness State Park (Emmet County west of Mackinaw City).

- Pointe aux Chenes, Hiawatha National Forest (Mackinac County northeast of St. Ignace).

- Big Knob Campground, Sault Ste. Marie State Forest Management Unit (Mackinac County southwest of Naubinway).

Uses and management

Aside from some local timber harvesting and hunting, dune-swale complexes are little used and generally not highly managed. Further preservation of unaltered examples of this unique hybrid community type is needed, along with interpretive signage, trails, and overlooks.

Northern Disturbed (Aspen-Paper Birch) Forests

Habitat

The forests of Michigan exemplify secondary plant succession following major disturbances. With the exception of a few small areas of virgin forest — now mostly protected in parks — the state's treed communities are second- or third-growth forests. The initial waves of logging that began in the 19th century laid low virtually every tract of timber that had any value, and the wildfires that followed repeatedly killed back recovering forests, with red pine, white pine, and hemlock experiencing the heaviest toll. The 20th century forests that finally grew back after the fires were controlled or when marginal agriculture was abandoned consisted of vast areas of early-successional pioneers that were exceptionally well adapted to establish on highly disturbed sites. A large area of this forest type still exists, although much of it has succeeded to more stable communities. Disturbed forests occupy a wide variety of landforms and habitats, from xeric to very wet-mesic, and they occur throughout the state.

Bigtooth aspen bark (left) is darker than bark of quaking aspen (right).

Signature trees

Three closely related species are the benchmarks of this type. Their ability to produce large quantities of cottony seed and sprout copiously from shallow roots make them ideal pioneers:

- **Quaking aspen**
- **Bigtooth aspen**
- **Balsam poplar**

Both aspens will grow in dry-mesic or mesic habitats. Bigtooth aspen is better adapted to xeric habitats. Quaking aspen and balsam poplar are more tolerant of excessive moisture, occurring commonly in wet-mesic habitats. They can even be found in seasonal wetlands. It is not unusual to find two or three of these species growing together.

Three other pioneers also occupied large areas following logging, fire, and agricultural abandonment, sometimes mixed with aspen:

- **Paper birch**
- **Pin cherry**
- **Eastern cottonwood** (primarily in Region I)

The light, wind-borne seed and stump sprouting habit of paper birch and cottonwood also make them ideal pioneers. The seed of pin cherry is spread mainly by birds and animals, and it can remain dormant in the soil for many decades. This diminutive cherry is particularly well adapted to revegetate burned areas.

Paper birch is more common in the Upper Peninsula.

Other trees

- White pine
- Red pine
- Balsam fir (subcanopy)
- White spruce (subcanopy)
- Many different hardwoods, depending on habitat and location; moderately tolerant or tolerant hardwoods will be subcanopy

Associated plants

Understory plants in these communities vary widely depending on the particular habitat (see, in particular, types 9-13). In many cases, the severity of the disturbances that led to the establishment of pioneer communities

depleted both the fertility of the soil and plant diversity. Michigan's Thumb region is a good example. Barring further stand-replacing disturbances, fertility and diversity will recover, although it might take a very long time.

Distribution and status

Well over 3 million acres of early-successional aspen-birch-balsam-poplar forests remain in the state today, a decline of over one-third from their peak acreage in the 1930s—succession has been at work. About 96 percent of the current area lies in the northern three regions. In Region I, the Thumb contains most of the small aspen-birch acreage. Aspen-birch-poplar area will continue to decline in the future; only active management or natural stand-

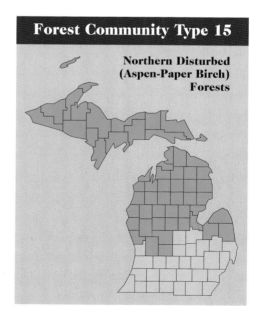

Forest Community Type 15

Northern Disturbed (Aspen-Paper Birch) Forests

replacing disturbances will maintain it at some reduced level. Because pin cherry is a small, short-lived tree, it also is much less common today than it was 50 to 75 years ago. Cottonwood has taken over much abandoned upland and lowland in Region I and is quite common, but the acreage it occupies is unknown.

Key viewing areas

- Huron, Sanilac, and Tuscola counties in Michigan's Thumb.

- Virtually any state or national forest in regions II, III, and IV.

Uses and management

Once considered useless by the forest products industry, the aspens—known colloquially as "popple"—are now among the most important timber trees in the state. Birch also is widely used, but balsam poplar and cottonwood have less value. These species are utilized mainly for pulp and oriented-strand board, although some lumber is sawn from them. Early-successional forests also provide some of the most important wildlife habitat in the state. Game animals such as white-tailed deer, ruffed grouse, and woodcock are very dependent on them.

An aspen forest succeeding to balsam fir and white pine.

Pin cherry.

To perpetuate early-successional forests, a stand-replacing disturbance must occur before the pioneer trees die. Today, this is accomplished mostly by timber harvesting. An aspen or balsam poplar stand can be clear-cut and suckers will sprout back from the roots by the thousands, creating clonal stands. But this extremely predictable practice has become controversial. Some people feel these forests should be allowed to succeed naturally to late-successional types such as northern hardwoods (Type 9), white pine (Type 11), or boreal conifers (Type 13). Paper birch also strongly sprouts if cut or killed, but from the base of the stem, not the roots. To enhance seed germination and seedling establishment of both aspen and birch, a hot fire or soil disturbance is necessary. In areas with high deer populations, young trees can be killed by heavy browsing; at best, early growth is set back until trees grow out of reach. Silvicultural thinning usually is not done.

Habitat

Trees have been planted in Michigan for forestry purposes wherever open land existed, usually abandoned fields or pastures and burned-over or cut-over tracts. Therefore, habitats vary widely. Most successful tree planting in the state has occurred on dry-mesic or mesic habitats. Some plantings also have occurred on very dry or very wet sites, but failure rates often have been high. Significant wildland planting began in the 1920s, reached peaks during the Civilian Conservation Corps era in the late 1930s and early 1940s, during the Soil Bank era in the 1950s, and, more recently, as a result of the Conservation Reserve Program. In recent years, between 25,000 and 30,000 acres per year have been planted in Michigan. Today, many plantations on open land are for Christmas trees, but these are more akin to agricultural fields than forests and will not be considered here.

Jack pine planting for Kirtland's warbler habitat.

Signature trees

The bulk of Michigan's wildland plantations consist of either one of two conifers:

- **Red pine**
- **Jack pine**

The area that has been planted with red pine is nearly double that of jack pine. In the past, the two species sometimes were planted in a mixture, but after 30 to 40 years, red pine overtops jack pine and the latter dies out.

Other plantation trees

- White pine
- Austrian pine*
- Scotch pine* (often abandoned Christmas tree fields)
- White spruce
- Norway spruce*
- Black spruce (rarely)
- Blue spruce* (rarely)
- Tamarack (rarely)
- European larch* (rarely)

Only three hardwoods have been planted to any extent, mostly in regions I and II, but their acreage is small compared with that of conifers:

- Black walnut
- Hybrid poplars*
- Red oak

Exotic (non-native)

Associated plants

Understory vegetation in plantation communities varies widely depending on the particular habitat (see, in particular, types 10-12). When the crowns of conifer trees in a plantation grow together, a very dense shade is created that limits understory development. In fact, the forest floor in many young closed plantations often is barren of vegetation. Only when plantings are thinned or when natural mortality occurs to open up the canopy will a vigorous community of understory plants develop.

Distribution and status

Plantations occur in every region of the state, with by far the largest area in Region II. They are particularly evident in the winter, when hardwoods are leafless. Although some older plantations are being harvested for wood products or are declining in health, planting continues, so these communities will be an enduring feature of Michigan's forested landscapes.

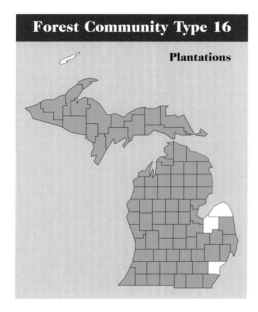

Forest Community Type 16

Plantations

Key viewing areas

- Hardwoods—Fred Russ Forest (Cass County east of Dowagiac).

- Hardwoods and conifers—W.K. Kellogg Experimental Forest (Kalamazoo County between Battle Creek and Kalamazoo).

- Jack pine—Kirtland's warbler plantations in the Huron National Forest and Grayling and Roscommon state forest management units (Oscoda, Crawford, and Montmorency counties centered on Mio); access is restricted during the breeding season.

Pine plantations often were established on deforested northern hardwood habitats; now they are succeeding back to hardwoods.

After thinning, mature plantations take on a more natural look.

- Red pine—the "Kellogg Block," Manistee National Forest (Wexford and Lake counties southwest of Cadillac), the largest contiguous red pine plantation in the country.

- Red pine, white pine, Norway spruce—the Beal Plantation annex to Hartwick Pines State Park (Crawford County on the east side of Grayling). Established in 1888, this is the oldest known forest plantation in Michigan.

Uses and management

Red pine has been planted mainly for pulpwood, sawtimber, utility poles, cabin logs, and, to some extent, for soil conservation. Jack pine was once planted mainly for pulpwood and soil conservation, but in past decades thousands of acres have been planted to create habitat for the endangered Kirtland's warbler. These efforts have been very successful, leading to a resurgence in the population of this singular little bird. Other trees—particularly white pine and walnut—also are planted for timber. But the role of many conifer plantings simply is to establish an evergreen presence on the landscape.

When plantations become fully closed but before natural mortality begins to occur, they should be thinned to concentrate diameter growth on the largest trees and maintain overall tree vigor. Commonly the first thinning is accomplished by removing every third row or two out of every four rows of trees. Subsequent thinnings at 10- to 15-year intervals selectively remove the poorest, slowest growing trees. When mature, plantations can be clear-cut and replanted. Alternatively, about half or two-thirds of the trees can be cut, leaving the rest to provide seed and shelter for natural reproduction. Some control of competing vegetation using prescribed fire, herbicides, or mechanical means is usually necessary before reestablishment of the planted species can occur.

Open forests of scattered or clumped trees—known as savannas or barrens—represent a transition between closed forests and prairies. They are maintained by frequent disturbances, usually fire or grazing. Trees are the dominant structural feature, but their low density and dispersion allow many plants typical of prairies and meadows to occupy the large gaps in the overstory. Forest understory species are more common in shaded areas. Although they occupied more than 2 million acres in the early 1800s, savannas are the rarest forest communities in Michigan today. In fact, the bucolic upland "oak openings" described by early settlers and by James Fenimore Cooper in his story of the same name have disappeared, as have the prairie chickens that occupied them. Because many savannas—particularly oak openings—occupied fertile mesic habitats, they were long ago cleared for agriculture. Many wet-mesic savanna habitats were drained or grew into closed forests. Urban development also claimed much of the area once occupied by open forests. Savanna communities in xeric habitats unsuitable for farming grew into closed forests when fire was excluded or when farmland was abandoned. Today state, federal, and private agencies are actively working to preserve or restore examples of these fascinating communities.

Open communities also can be the product of harsh habitat conditions (e.g., rock outcroppings) or human disturbances. Although these communities also are relatively rare, their total area in the state has remained fairly stable or slowly declined since Euro-American settlement.

 = **widespread**; type very common in one or several regions or throughout the state, with many examples close at hand.

 = **local**; type confined to a specialized habitat in a particular region or regions of the state, yet not hard to find.

 = **rare**; type very uncommon and highly localized in the state, with very few examples.

Habitat

Where present, this community type occupies poorly drained clay soils or sandy soils underlain by clay in the plain formed by meltwaters from the Wisconsin glacier. This flat or gently undulating plain extends inland up to 30 or 40 miles from the shores of lakes Erie and St. Clair and Saginaw Bay. Some of these lowland habitats are inundated in the spring, but during a dry summer they can become droughty.

Sandy former stream channels and dunes are interspersed throughout the lake plains; on some of these dry-mesic or xeric habitats, dry oak forests (Type 8) are found in association with the present type. Historically, these savannas occurred in a mosaic with sandy oak flatwoods, hardwood swamps, and wet or mesic prairies. The greater Detroit area and shoreline developments now occupy much of the southernmost part of this habitat.

Many former openings have grown into closed oak forests.

Signature trees

- **Bur oak**
- **Pin oak**
- **Swamp white oak**
- **Eastern cottonwood**

Other common trees

- Red maple
- Silver maple
- Green ash
- Quaking aspen
- Black cherry
- Shagbark hickory

Associated plants

Shrubs mostly are characteristic of moist habitats:

- American hazelnut
- Shining sumac
- Chokeberry
- Buttonbush
- Red-osier dogwood
- Pale dogwood
- Michigan holly
- Autumn olive*
- Blueleaf willow
- Heartleaf willow

Many of these herbs are character-istic of lake-plain prairies:

- Swamp betony
- Shrubby cinquefoil
- Common mountain mint
- Ohio goldenrod
- Riddel's goldenrod
- Blazing star
- Ironweed
- Black-eyed Susan
- Tall coreopsis
- New England aster
- Queen Anne's lace*
- Purple milkweed
- Butterfly weed
- Michigan lily
- Wood lily

Exotic (non-native)

Michigan lily.

Shining sumac.

- Big bluestem grass
- Little bluestem grass
- Indian grass
- Blue-joint grass
- Switchgrass
- Rush
- Twig rush
- Sedges

Distribution and status

Lake-plain oak openings are confined to Region I—the Great Lakes shorelines in Monroe, Wayne, St. Clair, Huron, Tuscola, and Bay counties. Although this type and its associated sand barrens occupied more than 75,000 acres in the early 1800s, its current area is no more than a few hundred acres. The rare occurrence,

Tall coreopsis.

degraded condition, and uncertain status of oak openings demand protection of existing tracts and creation of new areas.

Key viewing areas

- Algonac State Park (St. Clair County; mouth of the St. Clair River east of Pontiac)—degraded oak openings with some restoration in progress.
- Petersburg State Game Area (Monroe County southwest of Dundee).

Uses and management

These unique communities provide a glimpse of what a good part of pre-settlement Detroit was like. That alone

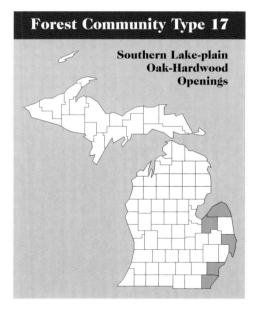

Forest Community Type 17

Southern Lake-plain Oak-Hardwood Openings

Blazing star.

canopy and subcanopy trees to create an open, park-like condition. Large, wide-crowned trees should be left, if possible. A major disruption of these habitats also has been drainage, so ditch filling or damming may be required. Reintroduction of regular pre-scribed fires is the next step. Tree sprouts and brush (especially exotic invasives such as buckthorn and autumn olive) will have to be treated with herbicides, followed by seeding of herb species whose seed bank has been depleted. Once the appropriate ground flora has established, moderate-intensity fires at three- to five-year intervals will promote the prairie grass-herb components.

Big bluestem grass, 6 feet tall.

makes them worth saving and expand-ing. The major management needed is restoration; in fact, some areas called "oak savanna" are in reality closed oak forests. Oak openings require frequent maintenance fires at intervals of one to five years, but fires have been excluded for a long time in all but a few areas. Overgrown openings under restoration require heavy selective cutting of

116

Habitat

This savanna community occupies the most drought-prone habitats in the southern part of the state—level or gently rolling, excessively well-drained glacial outwash or ice-contact landforms. Soils are sandy, infertile, acid in pH, and low in organic matter. Historically, oak barrens tended to occur in bands surrounding areas of prairie. They were maintained by regular fires set accidentally or intentionally by native people. Lightning fires also occurred. When Euro-American settlers came on the scene, these fires began to wane. Many acres that once were this type have been lost to human developments or have succeeded to dry oak forests (Type 8) because of the exclusion of regular fires. Farming these harsh habitats never was a viable option.

Signature trees

Two oaks dominate this type, with few associated species attaining their stature:

- **Black oak**
- **White oak**

Other trees

- Northern pin oak
- Red maple
- Black cherry
- Quaking aspen
- Bigtooth aspen
- Sassafras

Choke cherry

- Pignut hickory
- White pine
- Eastern red cedar
- Jack pine (very local)

Associated plants

The small tree and shrub layer may be almost totally absent in some places or dense and thicket-like in others:

- Serviceberries
- Choke cherry
- Wild plum
- Hawthorns
- Pasture rose
- Shining sumac
- American hazelnut
- Beaked hazelnut
- Dwarf chestnut oak
- Low sweet blueberry
- Sweetfern
- Sand cherry
- Prairie willow
- Bearberry
- Huckleberry
- New Jersey tea
- Common juniper

In these dry prairie habitats, the herb layer is profuse and distinctive, with grasses always an important component:

- Northern dewberry
- Birdfoot violet
- Sky-blue aster
- Tall sunflower
- Dwarf dandelion

Northern dewberry (red leaves).

- Pearly everlasting
- Blazing star
- False foxglove
- Prairie hawkweed
- Common St. John's wort*
- Tickseed
- Flowering spurge
- White pea
- Wild lupine
- Hairy lespedeza
- Wild bergamot
- Wood betony
- Common ragweed

- Spotted knapweed*
- Prickly pear cactus
- Pennsylvania sedge
- Nut grass
- Little bluestem grass
- Big bluestem grass
- Panic grass
- Poverty grass
- June grass
- Needle grass
- Hair grass
- Reindeer moss lichen

Exotic (non-native)

Distribution and status

Once occupying over 700,000 acres in Region I, this community has shrunk to a few hundred acres, principally in Allegan County. Hundreds of additional acres are in restorable condition in Cass, Branch, Livingston, Jackson, Washtenaw, and Van Buren counties. Maintenance of existing barrens and restoration of those that have become degraded should be a priority for the Department of Natural Resources and private nature organizations.

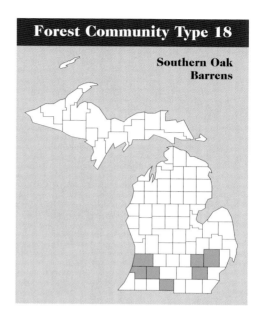

Forest Community Type 18

Southern Oak Barrens

Prescribed burning is needed to create or maintain barrens.

120

Key viewing areas

- Allegan State Game Area (Allegan County west of Allegan).

- Island Lake State Recreation Area (Livingston County east of Brighton).

- Fort Custer State Park/Recreation Area (Kalamazoo County west of Battle Creek).

Uses and management

Aside from hunting and outdoor recreation, this savanna community has no economic value. Its greatest value is the unique habitat it provides for flora and fauna. Numerous threatened or endangered species occupy oak barrens, including several butterflies, skippers, and moths. Most notable among them is the federally listed Karner blue butterfly, whose larvae feed only on wild lupine.

Little bluestem grass.

Prickly pear cactus.

Prescribed burning is the key management activity in existing barrens, with a one- to five-year interval between fires. Moderate-intensity fires at short intervals promote the native grass-herb component; low-intensity fires at intervals longer than five years will favor trees and shrubs. Restoration of degraded or overgrown barrens may involve heavy thinning of existing tree cover, leaving large, wide-crowned trees when possible; reintroduction of regular fires; and possibly seeding or planting barrens species whose seed bank has been depleted. The fauna associated with these singular communities will soon follow restoration measures.

Habitat

These diverse communities sometimes are separated into pine and oak-pine barrens, but in reality they share many characteristics, occur in similar habitats, occupy comparable geographic areas, and often intergrade. They typically occur on flat or gently rolling outwash plains, lake plains, and sand dunes. Soils in these xeric or dry-mesic habitats are sandy, acid in pH, relatively infertile, and seasonally droughty.

Barrens are the open savanna analog of dry-mesic oak (Type 10) and dry northern jack pine (Type 12) forests. The unique plant community of these barrens—in essence treed prairies—is maintained by frequent fires or by frost in depressions where cold air drains. The exact composition and structure of these communities vary by habitat conditions, past history, and geography from south to north and east to west. Some barrens once dominated by pine

are now oak dominated because of the intense and repeated wildfires of the late 19th and early 20th centuries. Trees in barrens can be large and widely spaced, creating a park-like look, or crowded and stunted in scattered thickets. Fire scars at the bases of tree trunks are common.

Signature trees

One conifer dominates many of these barrens (least of all in Lake and Newaygo counties), usually as bushy, open-grown trees or as spindly trees in dense thickets:

- **Jack pine**

Several oak species occur as large trees or as clumps of basal sprouts:

- **White oak**
- **Northern pin oak**
- **Black oak** (southwestern part of Region II)

Two other conifers are important, not so much because of their number as their large size:

- **Red pine**
- **White pine** (principally Lake and Newaygo counties)

Red pine was important historically in many northern barrens, occurring mostly as large "superdominant" trees that survived frequent fires, but it is less well represented today.

Sand cherry.

Other trees

Minor tree associates—the hardwoods often occur as sprouts—include:

- Red oak
- Red oak hybrids
- Bur oak
- Red maple
- Black cherry
- Quaking aspen
- Bigtooth aspen
- Sassafras (southwestern part of Region II)

Hoary puccoon.

Associated plants

The small tree and shrub layer is kept low and clumped by frequent fires:

- Serviceberries
- Pin cherry
- Allegheny plum
- American hazelnut
- Beaked hazelnut
- Low sweet blueberry
- Sweetfern
- Sand cherry
- Prairie willow
- Bearberry
- Huckleberry
- New Jersey tea
- Northern dewberry

In these dry prairie habitats, the herb layer is profuse and distinctive, with grass always an important component:

- Wintergreen
- Birdfoot violet
- Sky-blue aster
- Blazing star
- Prairie cinquefoil
- Hoary puccoon
- Prairie ragwort
- Divaricate sunflower
- Hill's thistle
- Canada hawkweed
- Gray goldenrod
- Showy goldenrod
- Tickseed

- Flowering spurge
- Wild lupine
- Prickly pear cactus (western part of Region II)
- Common milkweed
- Hairy lespedeza
- Pennsylvania sedge
- Little bluestem grass
- Big bluestem grass
- Poverty grass
- June grass
- Needle grass
- Hair grass
- Tickle grass
- Bracken fern
- Reindeer moss lichen

Distribution and status

The story of all barrens is the same. In the early 1800s, more than 380,000 acres of pine and oak barrens occurred in Michigan, mostly in regions II and III. Today only a few hundred scattered acres remain, a small fraction of the original area. Just like the prairie warblers or frosted elfin and Karner blue butterflies that inhabit them, these barrens are endangered. Restoration efforts designed to maintain and expand the remaining area of this community type are badly needed.

Hill's thistle.

Forest Community Type 19

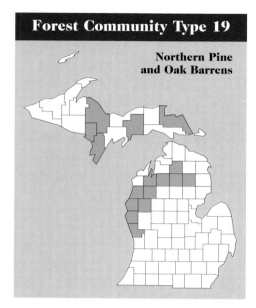

Northern Pine and Oak Barrens

Key viewing areas

- Coolbaugh Natural Area, Michigan Nature Conservancy (Newaygo County northeast of Newaygo).

- Valley Road Barrens, Mio District, Huron National Forest (Oscoda County southwest of Mio).

- Seney National Wildlife Refuge (Schoolcraft County northeast of Manistique).

- Shakey Lakes Barrens, Escanaba State Forest Management Unit (Menominee County west of Stephenson).

Reindeer moss lichen, prairie willow, and Pennsylvania sedge.

Barrens are an ideal habitat for bird and animal watching.

Uses and management

Barrens provide a refuge for the unique plant and animal communities that inhabit them. Several threatened and endangered species occupy open pine and oak habitats. Among them are several noteworthy birds: Kirtland's warbler, prairie warbler, prairie chicken, and sharptail grouse. Without barrens, these species and others will continue to be in jeopardy. Management of existing barrens and restoration of degraded barrens are accomplished as in the previous type (18).

Habitat

The shores of the Great Lakes contain many unique habitats. This community type is one of them. Occurring in wide, sandy depressions between dunes, these barrens appear almost desert-like. They can be associated with interdunal wetlands, however, and may, in fact, sometimes be former wetlands that have filled with windblown sand. The neutral sandy soils in these former embayments are typically xeric, but during periods of high lake levels, water tables may be at or close to the surface. The major disturbances are shifting dunes and human encroachments.

Signature trees

Several conifers and hardwoods occupy these barrens:

- **White pine**
- **Red pine**
- **Jack pine**
- **Northern white cedar**
- **Paper birch**
- **Balsam poplar**

Trees in barrens, like these red pines, often grow in clumps.

Associated plants

One or more of these low shrubs may be prominent:

- Common juniper
- Creeping juniper
- Buffalo berry
- Velvetleaf blueberry

The ground layer is typically sparse and may consist of:

- Bearberry
- Beach heath
- Poison ivy
- Cudweed
- Butterfly weed
- False Solomon seal

- Hairy puccoon
- Beach grass
- Dune grass
- Fescue
- Poverty grass
- June grass
- Nut grass

Distribution and status

These communities are very locally distributed along the shorelines of lakes Huron, Michigan, and Superior. Outside the protection of parks and reserves, their status is tenuous. Unregulated shoreline development and rampaging dune vehicles are constant threats.

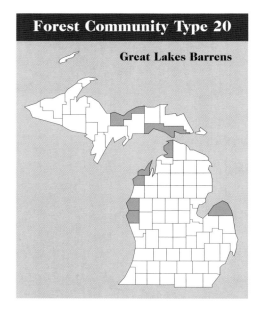

Forest Community Type 20

Great Lakes Barrens

Key viewing areas

- Port Crescent State Park (Huron County north of Bad Axe at the tip of the Thumb).

- Ludington State Park and Nordhouse Dunes Wilderness Area (Mason County north of Ludington).

- Sleeping Bear Dunes National Lakeshore, main land and South Manitou Island (Benzie and Leelanau counties northwest of Traverse City).

Butterfly weed.

130

Hairy puccoon.

Creeping juniper.

• Sturgeon Bay, Wilderness State Park (Emmet County west of Mackinaw City).

• McCauley's Point Preserve (southern tip of Donnegal Bay on the west shore of Beaver Island).

Uses and management

These fragile communities, which provide habitat for dune animals, are to be seen and enjoyed with proper respect. They have no economic use aside from human recreation. The only management necessary is protection from trampling, development, and dune vehicles.

Buffalo berry.

Habitat

Simply put, these are forests growing on rocks. Balds and glades occur on the thin, sandy soils of exposed igneous or metamorphic bedrock ridgelines and escarpments, which are not common in Michigan. On south-facing exposures, especially, the summer environment is very hot and dry. Cliffs—mostly consisting of limestone or sandstone bedrock—occur along the shores of the Great Lakes. Nowhere are these communities extensive. The forests that grow in these stressful habitats usually are open. Trees are stunted and bonsai-like, and some of them may be many hundreds of years old. The Germans call them *krummholz* (literally "twisted wood"). Often tree crowns on exposed ridgelines are shaped by the prevailing wind into a flag shape, with few branches protruding on the upwind side and most branches extending downwind.

Signature trees

A few trees are found on these rocky habitats:

- **White pine**
- **Red pine**
- **Jack pine**
- **Northern white cedar**
- **Red oak**
- **Paper birch**

Associated plants

Shrubs may include:

- Common juniper
- Creeping juniper
- Low-bush blueberry

Rocks are harsh habitats.

Trees, like these red pines, often are twisted and stunted.

- Nine bark
- Bush honeysuckle

Herbs:

- Bearberry
- Fireweed
- Three-toothed cinquefoil
- Bluebell
- Showy goldenrod
- Gillman's goldenrod
- Fescue
- Trisetum grass
- Poverty grass
- Tickle grass
- Hair grass
- Canada bluegrass*

* *Exotic (non-native)*

134

Distribution and status

Forested balds and bedrock glades are rare because the habitats that support them occur in only a few places in Michigan. They are found exclusively in the ancient highlands of the western Upper Peninsula (Region IV). Cliffs also are rare, occurring in just a few places along lakes Michigan and Superior in the Upper Peninsula. Rock forests generally are well protected in parks and reserves or by their inaccessibility.

Key viewing areas

- Fayette State Park (Garden Peninsula southwest of Manistique in Delta County).

- Pictured Rocks National Lakeshore (Alger County northwest of Munising).

Showy goldenrod.

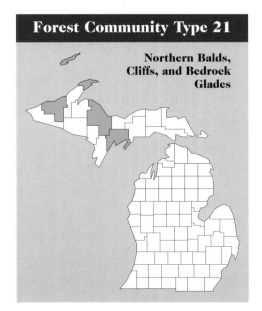

Forest Community Type 21

Northern Balds, Cliffs, and Bedrock Glades

Bluebell.

The Nature Conservancy

Bedrock glade.

- Porcupine Mountains State Park (Ontonagon County west of Ontonagon).

- Brockway Mountain (Keweenaw Peninsula northeast of Calumet in Keweenaw County).

- Mary Macdonald Preserve at Horseshoe Harbor, Michigan Nature Conservancy (Keweenaw County east of Copper Harbor).

- Isle Royale National Park (Lake Superior northwest of Copper Harbor).

Uses and management

These rare forest communities have no use except to be what they are— unique natural wonders. Their protection is essential.

Habitat

Alvars consist of flat, calcareous (limestone and dolomite) bedrock pavements lying close to the shores of the Great Lakes. They are harsh habitats, typically quite wet in the spring but excessively dry by late summer. This yin and yang of moisture is central to alvar ecology. The thin alkaline soils are deepest and bedrock is less exposed away from the direct wave and ice action of the lakes. Disjunct prairie communities tend to occur where bedrock lies at the surface and soils are thinnest (Catling and Brownell 1999). Plants tend to grow in fissures in the fractured rock, sometimes creating striking linear assemblages. Open savannas or patches of trees up to several acres in size intermingle with the prairies. Where soils are well developed, closed cedar-dominated boreal forests grow. Late-season fires were once a factor in these habitats, but today fire prevention and suppression have excluded this ecological process.

Stunted quaking aspens.

Signature trees

The scattered or clumped alvar savanna is quite distinct, with tree composition at any place depending principally on moisture availability:

- **White spruce**
- **Red pine**
- **White pine**
- **Balsam fir**
- **Northern white cedar**
- **Quaking aspen**
- **Balsam poplar**
- **Tamarack** (wettest areas)

Other trees

- Jack pine
- Paper birch
- Black ash (wettest areas)

Associated plants

Shrubs are common and may occur singly or in patches:

- Common juniper
- Creeping juniper
- Shrubby cinquefoil
- Fragrant sumac
- Choke cherry
- Buffalo berry
- Sand cherry

The ground flora is unique because it includes several state threatened plants, principally disjunct prairie and boreal species:

- Bearberry
- Lance-leaved coreopsis
- Northern ragwort
- Upland white goldenrod
- Ox-eye daisy*
- Large-leaved aster
- Hill's thistle
- Yarrow
- Spotted knapweed*
- Bluebell
- Bluets
- Indian paintbrush
- False pennyroyal
- Early buttercup
- Red anemone
- Blazing star
- Avens

Harold E. Malde

Prairie smoke.

Bromegrass.

St. John's wort.

- Early saxifrage
- Prairie smoke
- Prairie dropseed
- Poverty grass
- Blue-eyed grass
- Little bluestem grass
- Bromegrass
- Spike rush
- Bracken fern
- Evergreen wood fern
- Maidenhair spleenwort fern
- Brittle fern
- Sedges
- Reindeer moss lichen
- St. John's wort

* Exotic (non-native)

Distribution and status

Michigan alvars occur on Drummond Island, the Garden Peninsula, and several locations on the north shores of lakes Huron and Michigan. They are rare in the state, nationally, and worldwide. The Nature Conservancy, in fact, recognizes them as globally imperiled. An international effort is underway to document and protect them. Although some mining, development, and logging have occurred on Michigan alvars, most are under protection or otherwise not in immediate danger.

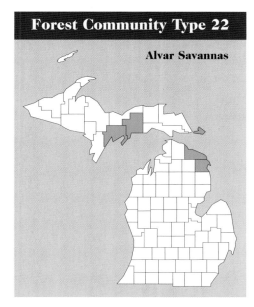

Forest Community Type 22

Alvar Savannas

Key viewing areas

- Thompson's Harbor State Park (Presque Isle County southeast of Rogers City).

- Maxton Plains Preserve (north shore of Drummond Island, extreme eastern Chippewa County).

- Southeastern tip of the Garden Peninsula (Delta County southwest of Manistique).

Plants grow in linear cracks in the limestone pavement.

Fragrant sumac.

Uses and management

In the past, some logging took place in alvar communities, but there is no need for that to occur in the future—less threatened forests can supply our wood needs. Because alvars become very dry in summer and fire once was a common occurrence, prescribed burn-ing may be needed occasionally to encourage fire-dependent species and thin out the tree cover. Because their plant communities contain so many state threatened or special concern species, constant vigilance is needed to protect alvars from mineral exploita-tion, lakeshore development, and mind-less off-road motoring.

Habitat

Once densely forested, these plains are a well known though slowly diminishing feature of the northern Michigan landscape. For reasons that are not completely understood, the forests that once occupied these habitats did not return or returned very slowly and piecemeal after the logging and fires that began in the second half of the 19th century. The venerable white pine stumps scattered across these prairies—many bearing char marks—are their hallmark. Yet adjacent tracts with similar landform and soil now support closed forests. These habitats once supported dry-mesic pine forests (Type 11) and, except for tree cover, are similar to them. Fire continues to be the major disturbance. Some entomologists have speculated that high soil populations of white grubs, which eat tree roots, have hindered forests from reestablishing. Frequent fires, drought, grazing, insufficient seed fall, lack of mycorrhizae (essential root-colonizing fungi), and presence of thick stands of grass, sedge, bracken fern, and reindeer moss lichen also may contribute to slow reforestation (Barrett 1998).

Signature trees

Trees invading these communities are mostly shade intolerant or moderately tolerant and adaptable to open conditions:

- **White pine**
- **Red pine**
- **Jack pine**
- **White spruce**
- **Black spruce**
- **Quaking aspen**
- **Paper birch**
- **Black cherry**
- **Red maple**

Associated plants

Scattered small trees and shrubs may include:

- Juneberries
- Pin cherry
- Sweetfern
- Low sweet blueberry
- Northern dewberry

Grasses and bracken fern dominate the herb layer of these plains—in fact, Curtis (1959) called them bracken grasslands. Several weedy aliens also are common:

- Trailing arbutus
- Pearly everlasting
- Pussy toes

The plains are prime blueberry picking territory.

Gray goldenrod.

- Orange hawkweed*
- Common fleabane
- Large-leaved aster
- Western sunflower
- Gray goldenrod
- Mullein*
- St. John's wort*
- Sheep sorrel*
- Wheat grass
- Timothy grass*
- Kentucky bluegrass*
- Canada bluegrass*
- Pennsylvania sedge
- Bracken fern
- Reindeer moss lichen

* *Exotic (non-native)*

Ever so slowly, white pine is coming back.

Fire was a frequent visitor to the plains in the past.

Distribution and status

Stump plains can be found through-out regions II, III, and IV, but they are far more prevalent in the eastern Upper Peninsula. They range in size from a few acres to extensive tracts square miles in area. Although many of them persist, their area is slowly diminishing as successional regrowth fills them in. Foresters also have planted many stump plains with red or jack pine, although many of these plantings have failed. Eventually—although it may take another century or more—stump plains probably will disappear unless manage-ment efforts are directed toward their maintenance.

Forest Community Type 23

Pine Stump Plains

Key viewing areas

• Hartwick Pines State Park (Crawford County north of Grayling).

• Kingston Plains, Shingleton State Forest Management Unit (Alger County northeast of Munising).

• Stanley Lake Plains, Shingleton State Forest Management Unit (Schoolcraft County northwest of Seney).

Uses and management

Stump plains stand as a stark reminder of the lasting damage that humans can inflict on forested landscapes. Yet some good can come of any-thing. For example, the rise and fall of Michigan's sharptail grouse—a bird of open country—and stump plains have been closely correlated. Beginning in the 1920s when unforested stump plains were common and still periodi-cally swept by fire, sharptails began to occupy these habitats. Huntable popula-tions of this fascinating bird existed from the 1930s through the 1950s. Today, with stump plain area dimin-ished by natural succession and tree planting, this bird is once again rare and hunting is prohibited. The restora-tion of prairies, savannas, and barrens now under way, as well as maintenance of existing stump plains, may help bring back the sharptailed grouse.

© Rick Baetsen

The plains are ideal sharptail grouse habitat.

© Rick Baetsen

Gray wolf.

*U*nlike plants, which are permanently rooted in the soil, animals move from place to place. Large, wide-ranging birds and mammals may roam about a territory that encompasses square miles and several community types in search of their requirements for food, water, cover, and breeding. The territory of small animals is more confined, usually encompassing just one or two communities. During the season when they are travelling between winter and summer habitats, migrating birds and mammals can be spotted just about anywhere. Additionally, some animals are cosmopolitan in their habitat preferences—their requirements may be met in various ways. A black-capped chickadee or a white-tailed deer could probably be found in any community described in this book. Certain other animals are very picky about their habitat and, unless migrating, can usually be found only in it. It is fruitless, for example, to look for Kirtland's warblers in anything but a young jack pine forest or river otters in uplands far away from a stream bank or wetland.

Because of their mobility and often ambiguous habitat preferences, I did not attempt to identify the animals most likely to be observed in each of the state's 23 forest community types. Interested bird and animal watchers can consult Baker (1983), Benyus (1989), Brewer (1991), and the MI WILD (Michigan Wildlife Habitats) CD developed by the Michigan Department of Natural Resources for more information on animal habitats.

Trees and Shrubs:

Barnes, B.V., and W.H. Wagner, Jr. 2004. *Michigan Trees, Revised and Updated*. Ann Arbor: University of Michigan Press.

Billington, C. 1977. *Shrubs of Michigan*. Bulletin 20. Bloomfield Hills, Mich.: Cranbrook Institute of Science.

Little, E.L. 1980. *The Audubon Society Field Guide to North American Trees: Eastern Region*. New York: Alfred A. Knopf.

Neal, J. 1995. *Identifying Trees of Michigan*. Extension Bulletin E-2332. East Lansing: Michigan State University.

Petrides, G.A. 1998. *A Field Guide to Trees and Shrubs: Northeastern and North-Central United States and Southeastern and South-Central Canada*. Boston: Houghton Mifflin.

Tekiela, S. 2002. *Trees of Michigan Field Guide*. Cambridge, Minn.: Adventure Publications.

Wildflowers and Herbs:

Case, F.W., Jr. 1987. *Orchids of the Western Great Lakes Region* (revised). Bulletin 48. Bloomfield Hills, Mich.: Cranbrook Institute of Science.

Cobb, B. 1999. *A Field Guide to the Ferns and Their Related Families*. Boston: Houghton Mifflin.

McKenny, M., and R.T. Peterson. 1998. *A Field Guide to Wildflowers: Northeastern and North-Central North America*. Boston: Houghton Mifflin.

Tekiela, S. 2000. *Wildflowers of Michigan Field Guide*. Cambridge, Minn.: Adventure Publications.

Thierer, J.W., W.A. Niering, and N.C. Olmstead. 2001. *The National Audubon Society Field Guide to North American Wildflowers: Eastern Region*. New York: Alfred A. Knopf.

Animals:

Harding, J.H., and J.A. Holman.1992. *Michigan Frogs, Toads, and Salamanders*. Extension Bulletin E-2350. East Lansing: Michigan State University.

Harding, J.H., and J.A. Holman.1990. *Michigan Turtles and Lizards*. Extension Bulletin E-2234. East Lansing: Michigan State University.

Holman, J.A., J.H. Harding, M.M. Hensley, and G.R. Dudderar. 1989. *Michigan Snakes*. Extension Bulletin E-2000. East Lansing: Michigan State University.

Whitaker, J.O., Jr. 1996. *The National Audubon Society Field Guide to North American Mammals*. New York: Alfred A. Knopf.

Birds:

Peterson, R.T., and V.M. Peterson. 2002. *A Field Guide to Birds of Eastern and Central North America*. Boston: Houghton Mifflin.

Sibley, D.A. 2003. *The Sibley Field Guide to Birds of Eastern North America*. New York: Alfred A. Knopf.

Black, T. and G. Kennedy. 2003. *Birds of Michigan*. Auburn, WA: Lone Pine Publishing.

Insects:

Milne, L., and M. Milne. 1980. *The National Audubon Society Field Guide to North American Insects and Spiders*. New York: Alfred A. Knopf.

Nielsen, M.C. 1999. *Michigan Butterflies and Skippers*. Extension Bulletin E-2675. East Lansing: Michigan State University.

Bland, R. 2003. *The Orthoptera of Michigan – Grasshoppers, Katydids and Crickets – Biology and Descriptions*. Extension Bulletin E-2815. East Lansing: Michigan State University.

* *There are many excellent field guides available, each with a unique approach to the subject. I have selected a few of my favorites and those widely available on bookstore shelves.*

Ninebark and pollinating friend.

Albert, D.A. 1995. *Regional Landscape Ecosystems of Michigan, Minnesota, and Wisconsin: A Working Map and Classification*. General Technical Report NC-178. St. Paul, Minn.: USDA Forest Service.

Albert, D.A., and P.J. Comer. 1999. *Natural Community Abstract for Wooded Dune and Swale Complex*. Lansing: Michigan Natural Features Inventory (www.msue.msu.edu/mnfi/abstracts/).

Albert, D.A. 2003. *Between Land and Lake: Michigan's Great Lakes Coastal Wetlands*. Extension Bulletin E-2902. Lansing: Michigan Natural Features Inventory, Michigan State University Extension.

Baker, R.H. 1983. *Michigan Mammals*. East Lansing: Michigan State University Press.

Barnes, B.U. and W.H. Wagner, Jr. 1981. *Michigan Trees*. Ann Arbor: University of Michigan Press.

Barnes, B.V., D.R. Zak, S.R. Denton, and S.H. Spurr. 1998. *Forest Ecology* (4th ed.). New York: John Wiley and Sons.

Barrett, L.R. 1998. Origin and history of stump prairies in northern Michigan: forest composition and logging practices. *Great Lakes Geographer* 5: 105-123.

Benyus, J.M. 1989. *The Field Guide to Wildlife Habitats of the Eastern United States*. New York: Simon & Schuster.

Billington, C. 1952. *Ferns of Michigan*. Bulletin 32. Bloomfield Hills, Mich.: Cranbrook Institute of Science.

Brewer, R. 1991. Biogeography and ecology. Pages 59-85 in R. Brewer, G.A. McPeek, and R.J. Adams, Jr. (eds.), *The Atlas of Breeding Birds of Michigan*. East Lansing: Michigan State University Press.

Burger, T.L. and J. Kotar. 2003. *A Guide to Forest Communities and Habitat Types of Michigan*. Madison: Department of Forest Ecology and Management, University of Wisconsin.

Catling, P.M., and V.R. Brownell. 1999. Alvars of the Great Lakes Region. Pages 375-391 in R.C. Anderson, J.S. Fralish, and J.M. Baskin (eds.), *Savannas, Barrens, and Rock Outcrop Communities of North America*. New York: Cambridge University Press.

Chadde, S.W. 1998. *Great Lakes Wetland Flora*. Calumet, Mich.: Pocketflora Press.

Cleland, D.T., J.B. Hart, G.E. Host, K.S. Pregitzer, and C.W. Ramm. 1993. *Field Guide: Ecological Classification and Inventory System of the Huron-Manistee National Forests*. Cadillac, Mich.: USDA Forest Service, Huron-Manistee National Forest.

Curtis, J.T. 1959. *The Vegetation of Wisconsin*. Madison: University of Wisconsin Press.

Dickmann, D.I., and L.A. Leefers. 2003. *The Forests of Michigan*. Ann Arbor: University of Michigan Press.

Faber-Langendoen, D. (ed.). 2001. *Plant Communities of the Midwest: Classification in an Ecological Context*. Arlington, Va.: Association for Biodiversity Information (www.abi.org/publications/midwest/).

Hoffman, R. 2002. *Wisconsin's Natural Communities*. Madison: University of Wisconsin Press.

Kapp, R.O. 1999. Michigan late Pleistocene, Holocene, and presettlement vegetation and climate. Pages 31-58 in J.R. Halsey (ed.), *Retrieving Michigan's Past: The Archaeology of the Great Lakes State*. Bulletin 64. Bloomfield Hills, Mich.: Cranbrook Institute of Science.

Kircher, J.C. 1998. *A Field Guide to Eastern Forests*. Boston: Houghton Mifflin.

Leatherberry, E.C., and J.S. Spencer, Jr. 1996. *Michigan Forest Statistics*, 1993. Resource Bulletin NC-170. St.Paul, Minn.: USDA Forest Service.

McPeek, M.T. 1991. Land, climate, and vegetation of Michigan. Pages 15-31 in R. Brewer, G.A. McPeek, and R.J. Adams, Jr. (eds.), *The Atlas of Breeding Birds of Michigan*. East Lansing: Michigan State University Press.

Smith, N.F. 1995. *Trees of Michigan and the Upper Great Lakes*. Lansing: Thunder Bay Press.

Sommers, L.M. (ed.). 1977. *Atlas of Michigan*. East Lansing: Michigan State University Press.

Voss, E.G. 1972. *Michigan Flora. Part I: Gymnosperms and Monocots*. Bulletin 55. Bloomfield Hills, Mich.: Cranbrook Institute of Science.

Voss, E.G. 1985. *Michigan Flora. Part II: Dicots (Saururaceae-Cornaceae)*. Bulletin 59. Bloomfield Hills, Mich.: Cranbrook Institute of Science.

Voss, E.G. 1996. *Michigan Flora. Part III: Dicots (Pyrolaceae-Compositae)*. Bulletin 61. Bloomfield Hills, Mich.: Cranbrook Institute of Science.

Wells, J.R., F.W. Case, Jr., and T.L. Mellichamp. 1999. *Wildflowers of the Western Great Lakes Region*. Bulletin 63. Bloomfield Hills, Mich.: Cranbrook Institute of Science.

LATIN NAMES OF SHRUBS, GROUND FLORA, AND EXOTIC TREES*

Agrimony..................*Agrimonia* spp.

Alder, green..............*Alnus crispa*

Anise root................*Osmorhiza longistylis*

Aster, arrow-leaved ...*Aster sagittifolius*

Aster, large-leaved.....*Aster macrophyllus*

Aster, New England ..*Aster novae-angliae*

Aster, panicled ....*Aster lanceolatus*

Aster, sky-blue ....*Aster oolentangiensis*

Aster, swamp............*Aster puniceus*

Autumn olive............*Elaeagnus umbellata*

Avens.......................*Geum* spp.

Baneberry, red ....*Actaea rubra*

Baneberry, white......*Actaea pachypoda*

Beach heath ....*Hudsonia tomentosa*

Bearberry ....*Arctostaphylos uva-ursi*

Bedstraw..................*Galium* spp.

Bedstraw,
   sweet-scented ....*Galium triflorum*

Beech drops ....*Epifagus virginiana*

Beggars tick..............*Bidens* spp.

Bellflower, marsh ......*Campanula aparinoides*

Bellwort...................*Uvularia grandiflora*

Bergamot, wild ....*Monarda fistulosa*

Betony, swamp.........*Pedicularius lanceolata*

Betony, wood
   (lousewort) ....*Pedicularis canadensis*

Black chokeberry .....*Aronia prunifolia*

Black snakeroot ....*Sanicula* spp.

Blackberry, common..*Rubus allegheniensis*

Black-eyed Susan ......*Rudbeckia hirta*

Blazing star ....*Liatris* spp.

Blue cohosh..............*Caulophyllum
                                    thalictroides*

Blue phlox ....*Phlox divaricata*

Bluebell ....*Campanula rotundifolia*

Blueberries ....*Vaccinium* spp.

Blueberry,
   highbush................*Vaccinium, corymbosum*

Blueberry,
   low sweet ....*Vaccinium angustifolium*

Blueberry,
   velvetleaf ....*Vaccinium myrtilloides*

Bluets ....*Houstonia* spp.

Bog laurel ....*Kalmia polifolia*

Bog rosemary ....*Andromeda glaucophylla*

Boneset....................*Eupatorium perfoliatum*

Buckthorn,
   alder-leaved ....*Rhamnus alnifolia*

Buckthorn,
   common.................*Rhamnus cathartica*

Buckthorn, glossy......*Rhamnus frangula*

Buffalo berry ....*Shepherdia canadensis*

Bunchberry ....*Cornus canadensis*

Buttercup, early ....*Ranunculus fascicularis*

Butterfly weed..........*Asclepias tuberosa*

Buttonbush...............*Cephalanthus
                                    occidentalis*

Calla, wild ....*Calla palustris*

Canadian yew...........*Taxus canadensis*

Cattail......................*Typha latifolia*

Chokeberry ....*Aronia prunifolia*

Cinquefoil, prairie.....*Potentilla arguta*

Cinquefoil,
   shrubby ....*Potentilla fruticosa*

Cinquefoil,
   three-toothed..........*Potentilla tridentata*

Clearweed ....*Pilea* spp.

Club mosses ....*Lycopodium* spp.

Columbine................*Aquilegia canadensis*

Coreopsis,
lance-leaved............*Coreopsis lanceolata*

Coreopsis, tall ....*Coreopsis tripteris*

Cow wheat................*Melampyrum lineare*

Cowslip, Virginia.......*Mertensia virginica*

Cranberry,
high-bush...............*Viburnum opulus*

Cranberry, large........*Vaccinium macrocarpon*

Cranberry, small ....*Vaccinium oxycoccos*

Creeping
snowberry..............*Gaultheria hispidula*

Cudweed ....*Gnaphalium* spp.

Currant,
swamp black..........*Ribes lacustre*

Currant, swamp red ..*Ribes triste*

Currant, wild black ...*Ribes americanum*

Cut-leaved
toothwort...............*Dentaria laciniata*

Dogwood, gray..........*Cornus foemina*

Dogwood, pale ....*Cornus amomum*

Dogwood,red-osier ....*Cornus stolonifera*

Dropseed, prairie ......*Sporobolus heterolepis*

Dutchman's
breeches ....*Dicentra cucullaria*

Dwarf dandelion........*Krigia* spp.

Elderberry,
common.................Sambucus canadensis

Elderberry, red..........Sambucus racemosa

Enchanter's
nightshade ....*Circaea lutetiana*

Enchanter's
nightshade, small ...*Circaea alpina*

Fern, bracken............*Pteridium aquilinum*

Fern, brittle ....*Cystopteris fragilis*

Fern, Christmas ....*Polystichum acrostichoides*

Fern, cinnamon.........*Osmunda cinnamomea*

Fern,
evergreen wood ......*Dryopteris marginalis*

Fern, lady ....*Athyrium filix-femina*

Fern, maidenhair
spleenwort ....*Asplenium trichomanes*

Fern, maidenhair ......*Adiantum pedatum*

Fern, marsh
shield ....*Dryopteris thelypteris*

Fern, rattlesnake.......*Botrychium virginianum*

Fern, royal................*Osmunda regalis*

Fern, sensitive..........*Onoclea sensibilis*

Fern, shield ....*Dryopteris* spp.

Fern, spinulose
wood ....*Dryopteris spinulosa*

Fescue ....*Festuca saximontana*

Fireweed..................*Epilobium angustifolium*

Fleabane, common....*Erigeron philadelphicus*

Flowering spurge ....*Euphorbia corollata*

Foamflower ....*Tiarella cordifolia*

Foxglove, false..........*Aureolaria* spp.

Garlic mustard ....*Alliaria petiolata*

Geranium, wild ....*Geranium maculatum*

Ginger, wild..............*Asarum canadense*

Goldenrod,
bluestem ....*Solidago caesia*

Goldenrod,
Gillman's................*Solidago simplex*

Goldenrod, gray ....*Solidago nemoralis*

Goldenrod, Ohio ....*Solidago ohioensis*

Goldenrod,
Riddel's ....*Solidago riddellii*

Goldenrod,
rough-leaved ....*Solidago patula*

Goldenrod, showy .....*Solidago speciosa*

Goldenrod,
upland white...........*Solidago ptarmicoides*

Goldthread ....*Coptis trifolia*

154

Gooseberry,
  prickly ....*Ribes cynosbati*

Gooseberry,
  swamp....................*Ribes hirtellum*

Grape, riverbank.......*Vitis riparia*

Grape, summer ....*Vitis aestivalis*

Grass of Parnassus ....*Parnassia palustris*

Grass, beach..............*Ammophila
                                breviligulata*

Grass,
  big bluestem ....Andropogon gerardii

Grass, blue-eyed........*Sisyrinchium* spp.

Grass, blue-joint........*Calamagrostis
                                canadensis*

Grass, brome............*Bromus kalmii*

Grass,
  Canada blue............Poa compressa

Grass,
  Canada brome ....*Bromus pubescens*

Grass, cotton.............*Eriophorum* spp.

Grass, dune ....*Calamovilfa longifolia*

Grass, fowl manna.....*Glyceria striata*

Grass, hair................*Deschampsia flexuosa*

Grass, Indian............*Sorghastrum nutans*

Grass, June...............*Koeleria macrantha*

Grass,
  Kentucky blue ....*Poa pratensis*

Grass,
  little bluestem ....*Andropogon scoparius*

Grass, needle............*Stipa* spp.

Grass, nut.................*Cyperus* spp.

Grass, panic ....*Panicum* spp.

Grass, poverty ....*Danthonia spicata*

Grass, rattlesnake .....*Glyceria canadensis*

Grass, rice ....*Oryzopis* spp.

Grass, switch............*Panicum virgatum*

Grass, tickle ....*Agrostis hyemalis*

Grass, Timothy.........*Phleum pratense*

Grass, Trisetum........*Trisetum* spp.

Grass, wheat.............*Agropyron
                                trachycaulum*

Grass, white ....*Leersia virginica*

Grass, wild rye ....*Elymus* spp.

Grass, wood reed ......*Cinna arundinacea*

Greenbriar................*Smilax tamnoides*

Ground pine.............*Lycopodium obscurum*

Hawkweed,
  Canada..................*Hieracium kalmii*

Hawkweed,
  orange...................*Hieracium
                                aurantiacum*

Hawkweed, prairie.....*Hieracium longipilum*

Hazelnut,
  American ....*Corylus americana*

Hazelnut, beaked ......*Corylus cornuta*

Hepatica ....*Hepatica americana*

Hepatica,
  sharp-lobed............*Hepatica acutiloba*

Herb Robert ....*Geranium robertianum*

Hog peanut...............*Amphicarpaea
                                bracteata*

Holly, Michigan
  (winterberry)..........*Ilex verticillata*

Holly, mountain ....*Nemopanthus
                                mucronatus*

Honeysuckle, bush....*Diervilla lonicera*

Honeysuckle, fly........*Lonicera canadensis*

Honeysuckle,
  swamp fly ....*Lonicera oblongifolia*

Huckleberry ....*Gaylussacia baccata*

Indian paintbrush .....*Castilleja coccinea*

Indian pipe...............*Monotropa uniflora*

Iris, blue flag ....*Iris versicolor*

Iris, dwarf lake ....*Iris lacustris*

Iris, southern
blue flag....................*Iris virginica*

Ironweed ....*Veronia* spp.

Jack-in-the-pulpit......*Arisaema triphyllum*

Jerusalem
artichoke ....*Helianthus tuberosus*

Joe Pye weed.............*Eupatorium
maculatum*

Juniper, common .....*Juniperus communis*

Juniper, creeping......*Juniperus horizontalis*

Labrador tea..............*Ledum groenlandicum*

Larch, European ......*Larix decidua*

Leatherleaf ....*Chamaedaphne
calyculata*

Leatherwood ....*Dirca palustris*

Leek, wild................*Allium tricoccum*

Lespedeza, hairy ......*Lespedeza hirta*

Lily, blue-bead...........*Clintonia borealis*

Lily, Michigan...........*Lilium michiganense*

Lily, wood................*Lilium philadelphicum*

Lily-of-the-valley,
wild.......................*Maianthemum
canadense*

Loosestrife,
fringed ....*Lysimachia ciliata*

Loosestrife, tufted .....*Lysimachia thyrsiflora*

Loosestrife,
whorled..................*Lysimachia quadrifolia*

Lupine, wild ....*Lupinus perennis*

Marsh marigold ....*Caltha palustris*

May apple ....*Podophyllum peltatum*

Meadowsweet ....*Spiraea alba*

Milkweed,
common.................*Asclepias syriaca*

Milkweed, purple.......*Asclepias purpurascens*

Milkweed, swamp ......*Asclepias incarnata*

Mint, common
mountain ....*Pycanthemum
virginianum*

Mint, wild ....*Mentha arvensis*

Miterwort..................*Mitella* spp.

Moneywort ....*Lysimachia
nummularia*

Mullein ....*Verbascum thapsus*

Nannyberry ....*Viburnum lentago*

Nettle, false ....*Boehmeria cylindrica*

Nettle, stinging..........*Urtica dioica*

Nettle, wood ....*Laportea canadensis*

New Jersey tea ....*Ceanothus americanus*

Nine bark ....*Physocarpus opulifolius*

Northern dewberry ...*Rubus flagellaris*

Northern
prickly ash..............*Zanthoxylum
americanum*

One-flowered
pyrola ....*Moneses uniflora*

Orchid, Arethusa ......*Arethusa bulbosa*

Orchid, coral root .....*Corallorhiza* spp.

Orchid, early
coral root...............*Corallorhiza trifida*

Orchid, grass-pink.....*Calopogon tuberosus*

Orchid, green
adder's mouth.........*Malaxis unifolia*

Orchid, heartleaf
twayblade ....*Listera cordata*

Orchid, northern slender
ladies'-tresses ....*Spiranthes lacera*

Orchid, pink
lady slipper.............*Cypripedium acaule*

Orchid, ram's-head
lady slipper.............*Cypripedium arietinum*

Orchid,
rattlesnake..............*Goodyera pubescens*

Orchid, showy
   lady slipper ....*Cypripedium reginae*

Orchid, tall
   northern bog...........*Habenaria hyperborea*

Orchid, tall
   white bog ....*Habenaria dilatata*

Orchid,
   white-fringed ....*Habenaria*
                                      blephariglottis

Orchid, yellow
   lady slipper ....*Cypripedium calceolus*

Ox-eye daisy ....*Chrysanthemum*
                                  leucanthemum

Partridge berry ....*Mitchella repens*

Pasture rose ....*Rosa carolina*

Pearly everlasting......*Anaphalis*
                                  margaritacea

Pennyroyal, false.......*Trichostema*
                                  brachiatum

Pine, Austrian ....*Pinus nigra*

Pine, Scotch ....*Pinus sylvestris*

Pipsissewa ....*Chimaphila umbellata*

Pitcher plant ....*Sarracenia purpurea*

Poison ivy ....*Toxicodendron*
                                  radicans

Poison sumac ....*Toxicodendron vernix*

Pokeweed ....*Phytolacca americana*

Poplars, hybrid..........*Populus* spp.

Prairie smoke ....*Geum triflorum*

Prickly pear
   cactus ....*Opuntia humifusa*

Puccoon, hairy ....*Lithospermum*
                                  canescens

Pussy toes.................*Antennaria* spp.

Queen Anne's lace ....*Daucus carota*

Ragweed, common ....*Ambrosia artemisiifolia*

Ragweed, giant ....*Ambrosia trifida*

Ragwort, golden.........*Senecio aureus*

Ragwort, northern.....*Senecio pauperculus*

Ragwort, prairie ....*Senecio plattensis*

Raisin, wild...............*Viburnum cassinoides*

Raspberry, dwarf.......*Rubus pubescens*

Rattlesnake weed ......*Hieracium venosum*

Red anemone ....*Anemone multifida*

Reindeer
   moss lichen ....*Cladonia* spp.

Rue anemone,
   false ....*Isopyrum biternatum*

Rush ....*Juncus* spp.

Rush, beak ....*Rhynchospora* spp.

Rush, spike...............*Eleocharis* spp.

Rush, twig ....*Cladium mariscoides*

Sand cherry...............*Prunus pumila*

Sarsaparilla, wild.......*Aralia nudicaulis*

Saxifrage, early..........*Saxifraga virginiensis*

Sedge ....*Carex convoluta*

Sedge,
   Pennsylvania ....*Carex pensylvanica*

Sedge, wide-leaved ...*Carex albursina*

Sedges ....*Carex* spp.

Sheep sorrel ....*Rumex acetosella*

Showy orchis.............*Orchis spectabilis*

Skullcap, mad-dog .....*Scutellaria laterifolia*

Skullcap, marsh ....*Scutellaria galericulata*

Skunk cabbage ....*Symplocarpus foetidus*

Solomon seal.............*Polygonatum biflorum*

Solomon seal, false.....*Smilacina stellata*

Solomon seal,
   hairy ....*Polygonatum pubescens*

Sphagnum moss ....*Sphagnum* spp.

Spicebush.................*Lindera benzoin*

Spikenard, false.........*Smilacina racemosa*

Spotted knapweed.....*Centaurea maculosa*

Spotted touch-me-not
   (jewelweed) ....*Impatiens capensis*

Spreading
  dogbane ....*Apocynum*
                      androsaemifolium

Spring beauty ....*Claytonia virginica*

Spruce, blue ....*Picea pungens*

Spruce, Norway ....*Picea abies*

Squawroot ....*Conopholis americana*

Squirrel corn ....*Dicentra canadensis*

St. John's wort..........*Hypericum perforatum*

Starflower ....*Trientalis borealis*

Stickseed ....*Lappula squarrosa*

Strawberry, wild ....*Fragaria virginiana*

Sumac, fragrant.........*Rhus aromatica*

Sumac, shining..........*Rhus copallina*

Sundew....................*Drosera* spp.

Sunflower,
  divaricate...............*Helianthus divaricatus*

Sunflower, tall ....*Helianthus giganteus*

Sunflower,
  tickseed ....*Bidens coronatus*

Sunflower, western ....*Helianthus occidentalis*

Sweet cicely ....*Osmorhiza claytonii*

Sweetfern ....*Comptonia peregrina*

Tall bellflower...........*Campanula americana*

Thistle, Hill's ....*Cirsium hillii*

Thistle, swamp ....*Cirsium muticum*

Tickseed ....*Coreopsis* spp.

Trailing arbutus.........*Epigaea repens*

Trillium, common .....*Trillium grandiflorum*

Trillium, nodding ......*Trillium cernuum*

Twinflower................*Linnaea borealis*

Viburnum,
  maple-leaved ....*Viburnum acerifolium*

Violet, birdfoot ....*Viola pedata*

Violet, Canada
  white......................*Viola canadensis*

Violet, common
  blue........................*Viola sororia*

Violet, smooth
  white......................*Viola macloskeyi*

Violet, yellow.............*Viola pubescens*

Virginia creeper ....*Parthenocissus
                      quinquefolia*

Wapato (arrowhead) ..*Sagittaria latifolia*

Water hemlock ....*Cicuta* spp.

Water horehound ......*Lycopus* spp.

White pea ....*Lathyrus ochroleucus*

Willow, Bebb ....*Salix bebbiana*

Willow, blueleaf.........*Salix myricoides*

Willow, heartleaf ....*Salix eriocephala*

Willow, prairie..........*Salix humilis*

Willow, pussy ....*Salix discolor*

Willow, sandbar.........*Salix exigua*

Wintergreen ....*Gaultheria procumbens*

Wood sage ....*Teucrium canadense*

Yarrow ....*Achillea millefolium*

Yellow trout lily
  (adder's tongue)......*Erythronium
                      americanum*

---

*The authorities for this compilation are Billington (1952) and Voss (1972, 1985, 1996).